Overture to Space

Overture to Space

by

MARTIN CAIDIN

DUELL, SLOAN AND PEARCE

New York

First edition

Affiliate of
MEREDITH PRESS
Des Moines & New York

Library of Congress Catalogue Card Number: 63-10347

Manufactured in the United States of America for Meredith Press

VAN REES PRESS • NEW YORK

this book is for

CONGRESSMAN JAMES G. FULTON

who, in the best interests of the United States,
takes nothing for granted.

CONTENTS

INTRODUCTION

The Age of Space began on October 4, 1957.

That is a statement.

It is not a fact.

By the calendar we began the space age with the launching into earth orbit of Sputnik I. Historians with a sense of irony have come to regard the impact of the Soviet feat upon official and public America as the Day of the Great Shock.

Sputnik I—a man-made object hurtling about our planet at 18,000 miles per hour—engendered no single reaction in all Americans. There were many viewpoints and many conflicting attitudes. The average American found the event almost impossible to believe. Deeply entrenched convictions could not easily be reconciled with the Communist wonder in the heavens.

To the average citizen, space flight lay beyond the edge of comprehension. He perceived dimly that any such effort was enormously expensive and complicated, and demanded extraordinary engineering skills. Our scientists had told him this again and again.

There could be little doubt that only a nation with the highest capabilities in technology and science could hope to achieve flight through space. These were characteristics not of the Soviet Union, but of the United States. This was not a matter of fact; it was a national article of faith.

In 1955, the President had announced a satellite program by the United States as a part of our participation in the coming International Geophysical Year. Project Vanguard had become a household word. Our magazines had run illustrated articles about the Vanguard satellite. Scientists had given speeches and lectures on the miracle we were about to bring to the world. Artificial satellites had become synonymous with American genius, technology, engineering, science, and leadership.

There had been vague rumblings about the Russians running hard and fast in the scientific world. But many scientists, especially those allied closely with the Administration, ridiculed the reports that filtered down to the public.

More specific action was taken by the Administration. The Eisenhower Administration clamped a rigid ceiling on the national military budget. Military officials begging for increased appropriations were told to function within the limits established for them. The Administration ordered an across-the-board reduction in basic research. Weapons programs carrying the highest national priorities were restricted from engaging in overtime work, and ordered to stretch out their production schedules.

The official word went out to play down Russian achievements. Not Russian claims, but Russian achievements. We threw a blanket over the Soviets' startling progress in developing their intercontinental ballistic missile. The fact that our long-range radar installations had tracked the flight of new Russian rockets, was placed under a secrecy clamp.

We built official secrecy into a wall that soared higher than the Iron Curtain. We pursued, in the words of the Congress, an "impractical policy of censorship." To keep Americans from being exposed to the facts, information released to the public was "at the mercy of the whims of officials in the Office of the Assistant Secretary of Defense for Public Affairs who decides what, at the moment, fits 'policy' and what does not." *

* "Availability of Information From Federal Departments and Agencies (Department of Defense); A Report by the Committee on Government Operations to the 85th Congress, 1958."

In a ringing indictment the Congress stated further that the

> . . . withholding of nonsecurity information . . . has been car-
> ried to an extreme degree, beyond any authority traceable to
> law or to the Constitution. . . . Security has been perverted as
> a tool for the manipulation of information. Nonsecurity infor-
> mation has been withheld solely on the ground that it could be
> embarrassing. The Department of Defense has attempted to
> govern and control the reporting of news in a nonsecurity area
> in order to produce a desired propaganda effect.

To say that the intelligence, military, and executive agencies of
the United States Government were unaware of the impending
launch of Sputnik I would be to beggar the truth. Despite the facts
available to us, as well as a series of statements by the Russians,
who released the size, radio transmitting frequencies, and other
data on their forthcoming satellite, the United States pursued its
policy of hard censorship.

Aware that the Russians were about to fire their satellite into
orbit, the Government called a hurried meeting of the National
Security Council. That meeting wrestled essentially with a problem
that had simply been swept underneath the executive rug. Should
we tell the American people, *now,* before the fact, of the Russian
shot about to be made? Or should we maintain silence—and then
see how well the public sinks, or swims, when faced with the hard
reality of the Russian deed?

The American public lost out in that discussion.

So, totally unprepared for the enormity of the Soviet Union's
accomplishment, the public was thrown into a new world. Not a
world of space—but a world in which, contrary to everything it
had been carefully nurtured to believe, it had to face the reality of
the technological giant that was the Soviet Union. Confusion, disbelief, and dismay—all these characterized the state of affairs as
Sputnik I rolled up its millions of miles into space.

The success in this official suppression of information led, in turn, to shock on the part of the Administration. The Administration was thrown off balance, not because of the Russian satellite (on which it had full details before the launch), but because of the wholly unexpected reaction of the American people (and other nations as well) to the Soviet success.

The Administration reacted in a manner characteristic of its performance before the orbiting of the Russian satellite. Faced with distasteful reality, the Administration chose to ignore it. And this decision was third in the series of shocks of the American reaction to Sputnik I.

"The Cassandras who had known what was coming and who had accurately gauged the impact," wrote Richard Witkin in *The New York Times,* "were not spared their share of post-Sputnik shock. They were appalled at some of the statements from high places. . . ."

The Administration demanded official deprecation of the Russian achievement. It issued strict orders under the severest penalties for noncompliance that nothing should be said that might reveal the technical competence of the Soviets.

> On October 9, 1957, five days after Russia launched the first man-made satellite, the military chiefs of the Army, Navy, and Air Force issued orders which barred discussion of missiles and satellites. . . . It must be remembered that the orders, all classified "confidential," barred discussion of the United States satellite program which the President had publicly stated was an unclassified, scientific project.*

Rear Admiral Rawson Bennett, of the Office of Naval Research, responsible for the trouble-plagued Project Vanguard, dismissed the Russian satellite as "a hunk of iron almost anybody could launch." On October 9, five days after the satellite went into orbit, President Eisenhower told newsmen that "the value of that satellite going around the earth is still problematical. . . ." He made it

* Congressional Committee on Government Operations, Special Subcommittee on Government Information, 1958.

especially clear that the Russian achievement "does not raise my apprehensions . . . one iota."

In response to a newsman's question about a lack of priority for American satellite efforts, the President replied that the Russians had accomplished their goals by utilizing not Russian, but German, science and scientists.

"From 1945," he said, "when the Russians captured all of the German scientists in Peenemunde, which was their great laboratory and experimental grounds for the production of the ballistic missiles they used in World War II . . ."

Our reaction to the Soviet satellite now embraced the telling of fables. For the sad truth was that the Russians had in fact not captured "all of the German scientists in Peenemunde." The truth was that the Germans had abandoned Peenemunde months before the arrival of the Russians. Major Anatole Vavilov led the Soviet forces into the rocket testing center. "Peenemunde," related the major, "was seventy-five percent wreckage." The scientific staff had vanished. Secret papers and documents were gone. The rocket development laboratories had been methodically smashed and gutted. Vavilov stated that he was under orders to "destroy anything that remained."

How do we know these things to be so?

The German scientists have been in the United States since 1945. The vital documents and records removed from Peenemunde have also been in the United States since 1945.

A note of dissension came from a leading scientist, Dr. Joseph Kaplan, who declared: "I am amazed that in the short time which they had to plan—obviously not any longer than we had—I think it was a remarkable achievement on their part." And what of the 184.3-pound payload of Sputnik I? Dr. Kaplan did not disguise his feelings. "This is really fantastic. . . ."

Unfortunately, the voices of Dr. Kaplan and a few of his associates passed as little more than a murmur in the hubbub of denials and deprecations from the Administration. On November 1, the President announced that in a series of speeches to come he would explain the issues emphasized by Sputnik I.

On November 3, 1957, the Russians launched another satellite, called Sputnik II. It carried into space a 1,120-pound payload, including a live dog named "Laika," who was recovered unharmed and lived a week before being painlessly put to death. This bioastronautics experiment in orbit was one which the United States would not match for another four years.

There was yet another cry, of anguish, which brought the calendar year of 1957 to its close. On December 6, at Cape Canaveral, the first Vanguard spurted white flame and lifted from its launch ring—but only for a moment. The thundering explosion and great flaming eye that glared across the Cape marked the futility of our country's first attempt to probe what lay beyond our world.

With every second, with every new orbit, Sputnik I had crumbled the walls of censorship and had ground down the myths of official secrecy. It also brought the average man to question seriously the myth that by some miracle nature pays special attention to the well-being and survival of the United States in defiance of the facts of life.

The men who had dreamed for decades and worked for all that long time to bring space flight to its moment of triumph were hurt and puzzled by the first days after the fact. These men had long believed that when the day came, the entire world would rejoice at the sundering of the bonds of gravity that chained man to the thin envelope of his atmosphere. They had believed this, and they were wrong.

They learned that a public not uninformed but misinformed could not possibly hope to understand the nature of the event. Understanding is not something to be snatched from a headline or gained overnight by a miraculous process of reading a column of facts. Unable to comprehend, the people of the world turned back to the everyday things of life. They had glanced at space, and that was enough.

Yet the very existence of the two satellites could not be ignored. The Russian origin of the satellites would not go away. Sputniks I and II did not remain merely the first satellites to go into orbit. They became a mirror—a reflection of reality and a clamoring, insistent sense of values.

In the weeks that followed the launching of the satellite, it became all too clear that before the satellite could be built, its course computed, its rockets created, a foundation must have existed—a bedrock of science and technology, of brainpower free to move within its own disciplined avenues, and of educational institutions able to send into that technological world the needed younger brains.

Of one thing above all we could be certain. Sputnik I was not the beginning of the Age of Space. It was merely the raising of the curtain for the first visible act in the new age. It took some time for us to realize that the cast had been in rehearsal, behind the Curtain, for many years.

What had happened seemed almost too much to believe, and it had rocked our cherished myths. The Russian satellite was only one small, albeit visible, manifestation of the truth dawning slowly among the American people. The new age had been spawned many years before that day of October 4, 1957. It was just that we were blind to its coming.

Overture to Space

CHAPTER 1.

ONE NAKED, MISERABLE MAN

SOME men contend that the conquest of space began when scientists first accepted as fact that flight beyond the atmosphere was possible. This to them was the first though faltering step, and there is much to this line of reasoning.

It is not difficult to believe that the distance between man's ears is often greater than the distance from the earth to the moon. But a whole world of difference lies between the ideas of men and the physical realization of those ideas.

One of the obstacles to establishing a clear avenue of man's activities in space is that too often we leave unanswered the basic questions of "What is space?" and "Where does space begin?"

The question may be answered in different ways. Although we have been hurling all manner of satellites away from our planet for nearly six years, we have failed to resolve the questions in a manner mutually acceptable to the many different sciences which are involved.

The man who wants to place a satellite in orbit about the earth defines space as beginning at the edge of the *aerothermodynamic border*. One hundred miles above our planet the wisps of atmosphere are so tenuous that we can keep a satellite for several days in its wonderful balance between centrifugal force and gravity.

But only for several days. In answer, the colleague of this first
scientist says "Nonsense!" And to support his argument, he uses
the ruling that space really begins, let's say, six hundred miles
from the surface of this world.

He is replaced in turn by the scientist who claims validity for his
argument that space begins where the radiation belts and zones
of the earth slowly fade before the greater onslaught of solar and
cosmic forces. The argument will likely continue with the protests
of the geophysicist, who talks of the effects of electromagnetic
fields in space. Very quickly we are approaching the moon, and
we must contend with definitions of cislunar and translunar space,
and by that time we are outbound to Mars.

These explanations—all of them—skirt the very heart of the
issue. They do so because they are all based upon mechanical
definitions, and presume activity solely on the part of nuts and
bolts pieced together. No matter the degree of electronic wonder
to which we may reach in building a satellite, the end result is
still nothing more nor less than a hunk of machinery. It is a product
of man, but it is not of the world of men. And therein lies the essential difference.

On this world there resides the race of man. It is a world with
a thin envelope of a mixture of gases: the ocean of air within
which man breathes, lives, procreates, and functions. It is an ocean
within which, with the aid of wings and other devices, man has
achieved a high degree of competence in flight. "Swimming
through the ocean of air" is exactly what man does when he soars
through this ocean.

The atmosphere to man is first and last his giver of life. It is
essential that this basic premise be remembered when we talk of
space and where it begins. The atmosphere provides man with
the means of survival. The oxygen taken into our bodies sustains
a process. It is not enough simply to say that we breathe air, for
we don't, not really. We burn air. We consume the oxygen in the
air we breathe, just as much as any heat engine burns oxygen and

gives off waste gases in the process. Man is essentially a heat engine, and with the energy he produces he sustains the processes by which his organs and tissues function, and his brain remains the wonderful thing that it is.

Remove the fuel for the engine, and the brain dies. And the life that is man returns to so much basic chemistry to be absorbed by the soil of his planet, as it has absorbed countless other beings who were abandoned by the spark of life.

Since this is a world and an ocean of air for men, space begins where and when earth's atmosphere no longer protects men. Physiologically, space lies not so very far above us. It lurks but a few miles over our heads. Any other boundary is simply an arbitrary definition, a borderline, as it were, of mechanical space. As long as this is a world of men, then space begins where unprotected man can no longer remain alive.

Storming the heights that loom far above the world has entertained man's thoughts and challenged his energies since he first scraped together the crude means to venture along the cruel and unforgiving vertical frontier. Man's conquest of space began when he first left the earth in the oldest aerial vehicle known—the balloon.

Long before the Wright Brothers ever took wing across their wind-swept dunes along the Atlantic coastline, men of science and adventure were floating in wonder and agony along the lower edges of space, a deadly world where oxygen is fatally scarce, where the sun is blinding but, paradoxically, unable to warm the human body. It is a world where the dense pressure close to the earth's surface has vanished, replaced with a lung-searing emptiness that sucks at life and smears the brain with irrationality, and then blackness.

To keep men alive in balloons drifting in ghostlike silence along the lower edges of space requires essentially the same techniques and equipment necessary to keep men alive a hundred miles higher —beyond the atmosphere itself. Oxygen, pressure, heating *and* refrigeration—these are the essential ingredients for survival in these regions. It does not matter if that protection is in the form of a multi-million-dollar capsule hurled into orbit by a giant rocket, or of a gondola suspended beneath the trembling lines that are attached to a filmy and swollen balloon.

The chain of development of the sciences from early balloon flights to manned orbits about the earth has no broken links. In our contemporary world of flaming rockets and speeds of three hundred miles a minute, it is easy to forget that man has been attacking space since the late eighteenth century.

The age of flight through space no more began on October 4, 1957, than the age of flight through the atmosphere began when some lonely and anonymous inventor of decades past hurled a balanced glider through the air. It had to wait until man himself made the journey, until man braved the elements in his first, faltering step. The first flight of a man in a heavier-than-air machine, propelled by its own source of power, guided and controlled by the man lying on the fabric wing, was no more than the most cautious of probes into a new environment.

If it is by the criterion of manned flight that we set the beginning of the Age of Space, then April 12, 1961, should merit our attention. On that day a man soared about the entire planet in the first sustained centrifugal flight in history—a flight of 108 minutes from start to finish by Yuri Alekseyevich Gagarin.

Yet, the aeronautical engineers and aerospace doctors of neither the United States nor the Soviet Union would willingly admit that man's flight through space began on April 12, 1961. They would more likely explain further that Gagarin's flight was the end result of years of careful and ever more daring penetrations upward from the earth. And that Gagarin was committed to his marvelous voyage only after scientists and doctors had proved that a man could survive all that was known about the environment of space. In terms of the environment of earth, Yuri Gagarin experienced only one sensation in flight that he could not investigate closer to the earth's surface—sustained weightlessness.

Men were in space before Gagarin's flight. They did not accomplish orbital flight in space, to be sure, but they did encounter, and survive, every other danger to which a man might be exposed in the explorations through the upper reaches of this world.

The yardstick by which our medical scientists chart the vertical course from the earth is the human being.

> We take one naked, miserable man [explained a doctor]. And then we begin to deny that unhappy creature the comforts to which his body has been accustomed throughout his life. When we reach certain levels where his life is endangered, we have reached another plateau where there is demanded an artificial replacement in order to keep that man alive. Before long, we discover that the various plateaus have all merged. We are so high above the earth that—physiologically—that human being is no longer within the world that has assured his life to this point.
>
> And at that moment, I don't care what yardstick you use, this man is in space. The artificial environment we must provide for him is absolutely identical to the same environment that would keep him alive and well fifty, a hundred, or a thousand miles away from the planet. We may change the external configuration of the tin can into which we have placed the man, and we may put it atop a rocket instead of inserting it into a winged vehicle, but you haven't changed a thing. He's in space, and he will die just as quickly—and, I should add, with the same agony—whether you call your tin can an airplane or a spaceship. It won't make a bit of difference to the sensitive, demanding, creature inside the tin can.

The proof of the artificial boundaries in the heavens—and the doctors assume that anything that does not go by their own physiological yardstick is artificial—may be found in the conflicting "official definitions" that our own country has applied to space flight.

If we take an unprotected human being and raise him suddenly to, let's say, fourteen miles above the earth—he will die in a particularly unpleasant fashion. In an instant his body fluids will become a seething, frothing mass of bubbles and outrushing gases. His stomach will bloat in a fraction of a second to grotesque proportions. The gases within his body will erupt with explosive force through every opening in the body. Blood vessels will rupture, his eyes will pop outward in agonizing fashion, and the terrible cold will assail his body with a billion flaming needles.

Such is the result of sudden exposure to altitude relatively close to the earth, and this scanty description is only a fleeting condensation of the reports from a few of the men who were fortunate enough to stand at the brink of death, and return. Too, these reports came from men who had reached heights less than the fourteen miles which we are using as our yardstick.

If we were to take the same man to a height of one hundred miles above the earth—the height at which men in spaceships have orbited the planet—the description would change not at all. We might assume the liberty of throwing in a stark and alien background with the velvety blackness of space and the unblinking light of the stars, but that is about all the license we could take.

As far as man and his frail body is concerned, he is in space at fourteen miles or at one hundred and fourteen miles. His survival in an artificial environment is not changed one iota. Yet we feel compelled to establish wholly artificial boundaries. The United States and the Soviet Union are parties to an international agreement that establishes space as beginning at a height of 100 kilometers. This is 62 miles above the earth, an unwieldy figure for American record-keeping, but necessitated by the metric scale employed by the majority of the world.

That the boundary established in this fashion is entirely artificial is revealed conclusively by the adoption of a conflicting boundary. The United States on its home grounds has decided that any flight by a manned vehicle to a height of fifty miles or more constitutes a flight into "space." The figure of 100 kilometers is ignored. By this second ruling, then, Major Robert White of the U.S. Air Force was awarded astronaut wings for his ascent in the rocket-powered X-15 research aircraft to a height above fifty miles.

It is a somewhat enigmatic definition, since at fifty miles, or thirty or forty miles, for that matter, the wings on the X-15 are useless stubs that no longer affect the vehicle's flight. Through these regions the X-15 is no longer flying. It is carried through a huge ballistic arc by virtue of the momentum imparted to it through the powered phase of flight—its rocket engine.

Alan Shepard and Virgil Grissom each earned their astronaut wings through a ballistic flight, a suborbital mission in space. Instead of the X-15, they were strapped into a capsule placed atop a Redstone rocket. The Redstone engine burns with half again as much power as the engine in the X-15, and it burns for a greater period of time.

Major White was restricted to a speed of 3,784 miles per hour, and a total engine burning time of eighty seconds. This speed was enough to carry the X-15 to a height of just below sixty miles.

By virtue of greater power and an extended engine burning time, the Redstone rocket lofted Grissom and Shepard to about 115 miles above the earth. The suborbital flights lasted about fifteen minutes from start to finish, and this includes the period of drifting earthward beneath the main parachute, a slow and cautious descent. By comparison, it took White eleven minutes from the time he dropped away from a B-52 mother plane to return to the earth, and his final portion of descent was made with the "slow" speed of about 800 feet per second before rounding out for his landing.

Had the arbitrary distinction of "space" remained at the international agreement of 100 kilometers (some 62 miles), Major White would not now be wearing his coveted astronaut wings.

And yet—had his cabin and pressure suit failed him at fifteen or twenty or thirty miles, he would never have returned alive to the earth.

Long before the term *astronauts* became a household word there was a unique group of men who were the first aeronauts to penetrate into the stratospheric regions above the earth. Their forays into a bitterly hostile world may be considered as much more demanding than the explorations we witness today.

Before we committed men to the orbital paths in which they rapidly encircled the globe, the robot vehicles that preceded them had returned virtually all the knowledge essential to designing their spacecraft and assuring their survival. The environment might be, and is, alien and dangerous, but it was not an environment completely strange to man. Its characteristics had been well defined and established, and the process of providing an artificial and protecting environment was a matter not of scientific breakthrough, but of sound engineering homework.

Compared with the first men who ventured into the thin, cruel air of the upper atmosphere, our astronauts are almost pampered and well cared for. They *know* that vehicles sent into the regions far above earth functioned well, are reported on in exhaustive detail for conditions, and they have, through experience and escape systems, more than a modicum of assurance of survival. This is exploration in a plush armchair, if we compare it to the tribulations of our early aeronauts.

Those men of yesteryear who carried out their dangerous flights for the purpose of gathering information on the characteristics of the upper environments and of observing the reactions of men exposed to those conditions conducted flights as scientific exploration and investigation.

The first known balloon ascent for this purpose took place in September of 1784, when the English surgeon John Sheldon began his swaying ascent from England with the intent of recording the effects of flight to high altitude on the human body. As Professor of Anatomy at the Royal Academy, Dr. Sheldon was particularly well qualified for his mission.

Unable to conduct an objective self-study of his reactions, Dr. Sheldon soon abandoned his role of the medical scientist and became, instead, a fear-ridden, quivering wreck huddling on the floor of his basket. With each moment of ascent, the thin walls of the balloon became even thinner, and his wild apprehension mounted. History must record this first scientific ascent with the picture of the good doctor prostrate and nauseous at the bottom of the balloon basket.

The long-awaited, deliriously welcome sound of the balloon basket striking the earth was not enough to release the doctor's death grip on the basket. Sympathetic friends pried Dr. Sheldon's fingers loose and carried the hapless physician off. Understandably, Dr. Sheldon abandoned forever his pursuit of high-altitude medical knowledge.

In the years that followed, there were further attempts to obtain scientific observations of the human being at great heights. But for some time such efforts were doomed to failure, and more than one scientific team that had departed the earth with all good intentions returned to the surface clad only in their underwear, having been forced by the terrifyingly rapid descents to hurl over the side anything that might regain buoyancy for their balloons.

The beginning of the nineteenth century brought success, and agony, to the small but determined band of aeronauts. In 1800 Robertson ascended from Hamburg, Germany, to a height of 21,-500 feet. This height demands oxygen equipment or pressurization to prevent loss of consciousness and possibly fatal results. Robertson's ascent to four miles emphasizes the lack of knowledge of the conditions that might be encountered.

This mode of ascent and flight to such heights represents an activity that few experienced pilots today would wish upon themselves in their most careless moments. Nothing is more aggravat-

ing, or terrifying, than for a pilot to be unable to command the
course, direction and movement in every phase of his flight.

The gases that carried these balloons into the regions of thinner air were contained within perilously weak fabric or paper
folds. Balloon design is essential to safe flight today, but it was
unknown then, and represented a by-guess and by-gosh system.

The balloons were subject to every whim and fancy of the air,
and what appears to an observer on the ground as a serene and
placid sky is often filled with jagged bumps and jolts that transform a balloon into a quivering mass about to collapse upon itself.
The wind carried these ancient and fragile aerial vehicles to any
possibility of destination. And the sheer thought of ascent to great
heights into a region of the unknown, on top of those dangers, was
enough to stop the bravest of men from ever contemplating such
ventures.

Robertson and a companion, during their flight in 1800, endured
severe pain and suffering. More than four miles above the earth
they soon fell victims to the lack of oxygen and to the many effects
of lowered pressure. They told afterward of the strange sensations
as their chests enlarged when they gasped like fish for air. Bitter
cold slowed their blood circulation. Their eyes bulged dangerously,
and they were wracked with pain from badly swollen lips and
knifing ear pains. Soon there was a crimson flow from their noses.
Nothing the men could do stopped the bleeding, and on their return to earth they found their faces and clothes caked with blood.

Later that same year, Gay-Lussac and Biot of France exceeded
Robertson's height by soaring to more than 23,000 feet, a flight
during which Gay-Lussac fell helpless to the floor of the balloon
basket. There, quivering from oxygen starvation, blue and numb
with cold, assailed by a blinding head pain, he seemed so close to
dying that his alarmed colleague descended at once.

The scientific aspects of such flights were measured not in the
exacting records of instruments, for men were not yet certain of

what they should attempt to record, but in the physiological reactions of the men involved.

Glaisher and Coxwell of England were the first to accomplish
what by modern standards was specifically a scientific-medical mission into the upper regions of earth. They made careful plans to
record the minute-by-minute events that might occur during their
ascent, and it is to their great courage and stamina that the fledg-
ling science owed much. The two Englishmen rose slowly to a
height of more than 31,000 feet—a height which, if reached in an
airplane, is almost a guarantee of death.

The circumstance that the balloon ascent is a slow process was
all that enabled these men to survive, a fact unknown at that time.
Because their penetration into the regions of bitter cold and scarce
oxygen was slow, their bodies accommodated slowly to the cruel
conditions. Had their ascent been even slightly faster than it was,
their diaries would also have been their epitaphs.

The two scientists maintained a running record of their pulse-
beats, noting their surprise at the acceleration of the pulse. It was
not long before their hearts began to pound faster and faster,
causing alarm, but not deterring the men from continuing their
flight. Their diary records the moments—scrawled in handwriting
that wandered across the pages due to the lowered efficiency of
oxygen-starved brains—when their hands turned from normal color
to an astonishingly clear blue. Soon their lips were the same hue.

The flight continued. Clouds fell away slowly beneath the balloon and dust layers on the horizon formed a clear, sharp separation of the lower atmosphere from the thinner air above. The
sky deepened in color, and the temperature plummeted. But in one
respect they were fortunate. The air remained calm, the ascent was
smooth and stately.

Thus, the moment when Glaisher doubled over with the pain of
severe nausea came as a complete surprise. At 24,000 feet he collapsed, body shaking violently in the severest agony. Frozen, gasping for air, nauseous, blue in face and hands, frightened, the two

men gasped out to each other their willingness to continue the ascent. At 29,000 feet Glaisher's face and hands were a sharp blue color; his eyes bulged as he stared through a sea of wracking pain. Helpless, he lay on the floor of the basket, gasping and heaving for breath; he could not lift his head or even an arm to signal his companion. But Coxwell could read the signs of desperation in his bulging eyes.

From some inner source of great strength, Coxwell struggled to his feet. Coxwell knew that death hovered but minutes away, that he had one opportunity and one only to pull the valve cord of the balloon and save his friend's life and his own. Moving arms that seemed coated with lead, he brought his hands before his face and stared in horror. Both hands were severely frostbitten, paralyzed with cold. Fighting for his breath, suffocated by a white flame in his chest, he struggled to pull the valve cord. Then he staggered to his feet, reached up. His lips split and cracked as he opened his mouth and clamped his teeth on the valve cord. Utterly spent, washed with pain, he pitched over in a crumpled heap.

Long minutes later Glaisher stirred back to life. He rested, gathered his strength. Slowly and carefully, he pried open his unconscious friend's mouth to release the valve cord. The balloon drifted steadily closer and closer to earth, assuring life.

The history of the brothers Gaston and Albert Tissandier is an unbroken record of cruel suffering and the undaunted facing of the elements far above this world. With their scientific assistants, these men carried out an unrelenting assault on the hazards, known and unknown, through which they were convinced other men in improved vehicles must one day journey.

Their equipment was the result of the most careful studies. Beneath great balloons they soared in gondolas equipped with scientific instruments to measure the changing characteristics of the atmosphere, telescopes and other devices. Their story is a detailed one of scientific labors, but it would be incomplete without noting that on many occasions they returned to earth with their instruments caked with their own blood and vomitus.

The good fortune, the touch of benevolent faith that every pilot wishes to be his for a while also attended the Tissandiers and their companions in their endeavors. In 1875 they soared to a height estimated at more than 30,000 feet. Only an estimate could be made, for the four men on the mission collapsed within seconds of one another and fell to the balloon basket floor. By some miracle, the balloon valve opened and the gas within began to flow rapidly from the swollen bag. The men regained their senses as they descended, and it was with a growing sense of wonder that they comprehended their recall from certain death.

It was on a subsequent flight that the explorers paid the penalties for journeying along the floor of the stratosphere without adequate protection. The balloon rose with its crew of three—H. T. Sivel, J. E. Crocé-Spinelli, and Gaston Tissandier—to 27,950 feet. The temperature dropped to a measured 62 degrees below zero, and then the instruments froze solid. Yet, until this moment, the men did not suffer. On the floor of the balloon basket were three flasks filled with oxygen, and from each flask a slim tube led to one of the men so that he could suck on the precious gas. Twenty-three thousand feet above the earth an elated Sivel scribbled with a gloved hand, "I am inhaling oxygen, the effect is excellent."

A half-mile higher, the brief note of euphoria vanished as the last of the oxygen hissed from the flasks. The "disease," hypoxia (oxygen starvation), of high altitude struck mercilessly. Minutes later the balloon leveled off, nearly six miles above the earth.

Within the basket, there was no sound. In the almost complete silence at the edge of the stratosphere, the balloon sailed the tides of the winds. The white frosty vapor of breathing showed, but it steamed from the face of one man only. Tissandier lay crumpled in a heap, unconscious and barely alive. The two scientists with him did not move. Tissandier was still unconscious and more dead than alive when the balloon finally drifted to earth. For weeks he hung on the brink of death, and then began his slow and painful recovery.

No man proved more conclusively the benefits of accumulated knowledge and experience than Germany's Professor Berson, who made meticulous studies of the problems and the disasters that befell the aeronauts. Berson went at his own flights with methodical thoroughness. And so in 1894, resembling a squat, furry animal beneath his multiple layers of clothing, and surrounded in his balloon gondola with oxygen bottles, Berson rose to more than 30,000 feet.

The professor remained at this height in his open gondola for more than five hours. Cold but not in pain, sucking on a tube which carried oxygen to him, Berson drifted silently along the fringes of the strange and timeless world.

Seven years later Berson and Dr. R. J. Suring of Berlin's Royal Meteorological Institute sailed away from the earth. On July 31, 1901, these two men became the first explorers of earth's high regions to penetrate into the stratosphere. Their giant balloon *Preussen* sailed higher and higher, surging away from the dense air near the earth's surface, until it eased its ascent at 35,424 feet, or nearly seven miles. Berson and Suring remained aloft for hours, returning safely to earth in triumph.

Fifty-seven years later, in August 1958, Major David G. Simons, chief of the Space Biology Branch of the Air Force Aero Medical Laboratory, also rose from the earth's surface. Simons rose not in an open gondola, but in an elaborate, expensive, highly advanced and complex pressurized capsule.

Major Simons' capsule soared higher and higher until finally it reached the peak of its ascent. The ghostly winds in the near vacuum at a height of 103,000 feet embraced the balloon, and gently carried balloon and capsule along the top of the world.

Outside the thin walls of the pressurized capsule there pressed an environment that, to the human body, was as close to deep space as one could imagine. Less than one percent of the earth's atmosphere remained at this height. If the environment was not technically "space," it was even to the most demanding of scientists admittedly a cruel and unforgiving "space-equivalent environment."

Three years before centrifugal flight about the earth was to be accomplished by man, Major Simons, as had other men who shared the same manner of his explorations, came to know intimately of space conditions. Thus, he could state of his mission in fact that "in respect to near vacuum, incoming radiation, heat balance and control, and in psychological preparation, the balloon capsule actually simulated satellite conditions."

From first-hand experience, the Major somberly described "the remoteness of the environment . . . emphasized by its totally different appearance: the lack of readily noticeable sky above, the strange colors along the horizon, and the almost incomprehensible large ball of earth beneath."

Major Simons remained at the shores of space for more than a full day, and exclaimed about the "strange, beautiful world" into which he had intruded. After the flight to the dark side of the earth and a long, long night, there came the sunrise:

> Against the brilliance of the clouds below when viewed in the direction of the sun, the blackness of the sky gave the impression of no sky at all, just an empty void.
>
> It was a strangely beautiful, bewitching world that I must now leave. A world that for all its exquisite beauty could be just as vicious and hostile as it was inspiring.

CHAPTER 2.

THE ROCKY ROAD TO SPACE

WE live in an ocean, yet we are strangers to most of its wonders. We live here at the bottom of this great and swirling ocean of air, knowing but a few of its miracles, its delights and its savage dangers.

High above the bottom of this ocean there glide strange and beautiful creatures of which we are, sadly, unaware. In the raw and naked regions of the stratosphere there are thin cirrus clouds. They rush over the surface of the world with a motion sometimes lazy and calm and at other times in a frenzied dash at hundreds of miles per hour.

Sometimes, no one can say why, these cirrus clouds change their form. As though flicked by a sorcerer's wand, they dissolve from their familiar shapes in an unbelievable blur and are transformed into sparkling, gleaming showers of ice crystals. Suddenly the entire sky is filled with billions of tiny, dazzling motes of golden and silver light. In all directions—around the entire sweep of the horizon, above and below, everywhere—all that can be seen is this wondrous display of the tiniest of blazing diamonds. Only a few men have been privileged to witness this silent wonder, and they have returned to the world of men with awe in their eyes.

And this wonder is but one of the many flickers of sorcery and rampaging energy which fill our "quiescent" atmosphere. The ghosts along the shores of space are sometimes visible to us. Fifteen or twenty miles above the surface of the earth waft the mother-of-pearl fingers of ice crystals which we call nacreous clouds. They sweep around the planet in an almost complete vacuum, their beauty and strangeness almost unknown to the human race that goes from day to day with no cognizance of these silent voyagers.

Even these are not the upper limit of the visible, physical wonders of the heavens. More than 250,000 feet above the earth there sail the beautiful filaments known as noctilucent clouds. Our descriptive titles seem sadly lacking, for these are not truly clouds, but gossamer wraiths of dust, or perhaps dust and ice crystals, or some other unfamiliar substance. Whatever their substance, millions of people have seen them and never known that they were witness to terrestrial travelers so high up that, by "official definition," they are truly clouds drifting in space. We see them only when nature lets the distant, setting sun spray the heavens with long beams of light. Only at these moments, when everything fits into a neat pattern of the clouds appearing in the heavens, while there is darkness on the earth (shortly after sunset), are these clouds transformed by the solar fire into blazing wreaths of flame— clouds in space that hurtle around the earth at more than four hundred miles per hour.

The ocean that surrounds this planet and provides us with a means of life is not simply an ocean of gases swirling about in an atmospheric mass. It is a deep and powerful ocean of electrical energy, of magnetic forces, and of great clashes of energy. There are many occasions when we witness these awesome energy displays, the most frequent being of course, the thundering roll of electrical storms. It is strange to realize, however, that only in recent years, accompanying, as it were, our invasion of the space beyond the atmosphere, have we really begun to comprehend the nature of the forces all about us.

It took the flight of a man in orbit, Lt. Colonel John H. Glenn, Jr., to confirm to scientists that from the vantage point of 150 miles above the world, it was possible to see the flickering tongues of lightning spreading from one storm front to another, spearing with forked tongues of energy distances of hundreds of miles.

In our attempts to ferret out more and more knowledge of this protective but also violent atmospheric mantle about us, we have gained a new perception of earth's ocean of air. We have come to appreciate the great storms of celestial energy that rain down upon this planet: energy from the sun and from unknown sources that lie unfathomable distances from the earth in the stellar regions. We have gained the slightest hint of the great magnetic forces that sweep as waves through the planet, and that interact with similar troughs of energy pulsing through space. We have gained keener insight into the cascade of stony and metallic objects that plunge into our atmosphere, fortunately to be rendered into dust by the friction of their meteoric passage through our atmosphere of swirling gases.

Sometimes, we see shimmering draperies in the skies, marching lines of glowing colors, waves that pulsate and glow. We see the great aurora, and our attention shifts from aesthetic appreciation to the determination of our scientists to understand the nature of the electrical particles that transform night into these muted pyrotechnic displays.

We have learned much, but above all, as we have achieved flight beyond the atmosphere, we have learned that this same atmosphere is a barrier to achieving centrifugal flight around the world.

It is hard to comprehend the nature, the incredible diversity and the savageness of the dangers that lurk within this multilayered barrier. We have become accustomed to thinking of the atmosphere in the terms to which the press has exposed us in the excitement of witnessing the flights of astronauts from Cape Canaveral.

An enormous rocket stands on the ground, its flanks covered

with frost. The ground below swirls with the vapors of liquid oxygen and with the most meaningful sound on the Cape, the shrill screaming of warm pipes as they react to the touch of liquids so cold that they boil at three hundred degrees below zero. The *countdown* has become an honored household word, a babble in our songs, the cry of children at play.

From the cry of "Zero!" in the countdown here on the surface of the earth to the reality of flight in orbit is a period only of some three hundred seconds. From liftoff to separation from the booster takes only five minutes. How thick is our atmosphere? How deep are its dangers? Only three hundred seconds' worth by the chant of the control center.

These three hundred seconds are the final culmination of many years of grueling work, of wild terror, of patient hours of study and planning, of billions of dollars spent. The five minutes of flaming gases spilling backward from the uprushing rocket are nothing more than the proof of all that has gone by, the triumphant vindication of lives lost and bodies broken.

You can walk along the streets of Edwards Air Force Base in California, on the scorched and baked edges of the Mojave Desert, and you can read the street signs of agony, of death by burning alive, of bodies ripped into fragments, of funereal pyres of smoke drifting lazily upward from the shining expanses of sand. The streets are named for men. And every one of those men died in the attempts to tame the invisible reefs and storms, reefs against which men in untried, dangerous machines hurled themselves. Every death here at Edwards, and at the many other testing sites in this country, and in England, Germany and Russia, built another step leading upward. Every time a man died, we were squeezing Time. Every time the call went out for a replacement, we were closer to those miraculous three hundred seconds that would signify the silent, weightless plunge of a man around the planet at 18,000 miles per hour.

The aeronauts struck the first notes of the overture to space as they ascended in their swaying balloons toward the unknown environment above them. But what they accomplished was not enough. Theirs was flight uncontrolled by man. If we were to aim toward a destiny of our own making, control was imperative. The aviators took over from the aeronauts.

Ad Inexplorata: Toward the Unknown . . . Its colors peeling in the harsh sun of the California desert, this is the sign that graces the test pilot quarters of the Air Force Flight Test Center. It is the terse but meaningful code by which test pilots today, as for decades past, hammer down the barriers to greater speed and heights for other men who wish to traverse the skies.

Flight through space was not the challenge. Indeed, once a man in a modern spacecraft has achieved orbit, he has also climbed free of the terrible dangers of space flight and, so to speak, sits upon a ledge of safety while the dangers swirl madly well below his feet.

It is not space flight that is dangerous—the danger lies in the process of ascending from the earth through the atmospheric barrier with all its reefs and hazards, and later, returning through that same atmosphere. Once a man is in orbit, his vessel providing him with air to breathe, with pressure, with temperature control, all his necessities of life are met. Any high-altitude airplane provides him with exactly the same sustenance. The critical difference is that any airplane must at all times continue to brave the reefs in the sky. The spacecraft has climbed to safety, beyond the physical and turbulent barrier that is our atmosphere. Achievement of orbit by the astronaut is a celestial sigh of relief. At that point, the space-craft is moving so swiftly and so high above the earth that it cannot come to harm.

The question most often asked about manned orbital flight is: "What keeps the spacecraft up?" The answer is, paradoxically, that nothing keeps it up. The law of gravity cannot be repealed. That law demands that any object within the earth's gravitational field must be drawn toward the center of the earth. A satellite, manned or unmanned, in orbit about the earth obeys that law. It obeys the law implicitly, and this is what keeps the spacecraft in orbit and allows the man aboard a clear measure of safety.

Picture the earth's surface. It is a sphere. No more than a hundred miles above the planet the curvature of the horizon is sharply defined. When we propel a spacecraft into orbit at nearly 18,000 miles per hour, we do so only when that spacecraft is moving parallel to the horizon directly below.

At a specific moment in space—let us say, one hundred miles high and moving parallel to the surface of the earth—our spacecraft has reached nearly 18,000 miles per hour. The moment the rocket's thrust is cut off and that spacecraft is no longer propelled forward, it begins to fall. It obeys the law of gravity. But there remains that tremendous forward velocity. The spacecraft begins to fall; however, it is moving so fast that it falls in the shallowest of curves. If we could stand well back and see both the curvature of the earth and the spacecraft's arc of fall, it would be possible to see that the two lines, the horizon and the arc of fall, match one another.

As fast as the spacecraft falls in its long, shallow curve, the earth curves away beneath the spacecraft. It is a fine and wonderful balance. So the spacecraft falls, and the surface of the earth falls away beneath it.

To the pilot of an airplane, this one fact alone is a miraculous freedom from the danger that constantly faces every pilot while he is airborne—falling. An aircraft is sustained by both the aerodynamic lift of its wings and the power of its engines. If either is interrupted or eliminated, the machine will fall. A spacecraft, however, may orbit in any attitude—flying sideways, rolling, tumbling —it doesn't matter. As long as nothing interferes with the spacecraft's free fall—and nothing will as long as it remains above the mass of the atmosphere—the astronaut enjoys a delightful freedom from the tribulations that attend the flight of the pilot.

The airplane must sustain both aerodynamic lift and power,

and more than these as well. Any machine that moves through the air is an antigravity device. The airplane must direct its aerodynamic lift in such a manner that it opposes the downward pull of gravity. Thus the airplane must always maintain, in addition to lift and thrust from its engine, a specific attitude in flight. Unlike the spacecraft, the airplane cannot simply tumble or wander about on its three axes (pitch, yaw, roll) of motion.

This does not mean that the astronaut is unaware of the problems which attend the flight of his pilot friends. The astronaut is first and foremost a pilot. His background is one of flight. More to the point, to reach his safety ledge above the atmosphere and its reefs, he has had to climb out of the atmosphere. And he still must never for a moment forget his return path.

Test pilots consider themselves to be men who on many occasions must "fly blind." They must penetrate into zones and areas of the sky which are so transformed by their speed, by compressibility and heat, and by other factors yet unknown to engineers and scientists, that they become savage in their effects upon machine and man.

The atmosphere under certain conditions becomes an environment not of this world, an environment that is unbelievably deadly and filled with countless snares for the unwary. We are familiar with wind, which is simply air in motion. But it is one thing to experience wind here on the surface of the earth, and quite something else again to experience winds that blow at thousands of miles per hour.

A wind of seventy-five miles per hour is a hurricane. A wind of three hundred miles per hour is the shock wave of a nuclear explosion. A wind of one thousand miles per hour becomes a shock wave hammering against the resisting atmosphere with such brutal force that it becomes incandescent. The frontal wave of that shock line literally burns. A sustained wind at one thousand miles per hour will level everything on the surface of the earth. It is not a "wind" in the ordinary sense. It is a juggernaut grinding down everything in its path.

Yet our test pilots plunged through the atmosphere at speeds of thousands of miles per hour. An aircraft moving with such speed through the air *does not fly* as we understand flying. It literally smashes and pounds its way through the air. It rams against a mass that fights its every inch of movement, that grinds and scrapes against metal with such terrible energy that the airplane finally glows a brilliant cherry red from heat. If you were to touch the surface of one of these aircraft, your flesh, blood and bone would be instantly vaporized into incandescent gas.

This is the world of the airman who built the long, bloody road into space.

To reach out into space, a man must learn to move through the atmosphere at tremendous speed. Men have been flying at increasingly higher speeds since the end of World War II, especially since October 14, 1947. That day marks the destruction of a barrier—that was the day that man first penetrated safely the sonic barrier.

Today nearly every fighter airplane is capable of flight at speeds greater than the speed of sound. Even our bombers ride the heavens at speeds twice that of sound.

For many years men tried to plunge through the barrier reef in the sky that stood at the speed of sound. Some of them made it. None of them came back alive. An invisible enemy in the heavens ripped with steel talons at their machines. The airplanes thrummed with a vibration that paralyzed the pilot. Metal shook and bent and rippled unbelievably. Steel wings fluttered like rags. Controls froze solid. These machines pushed faster and faster through the skies and, suddenly, with no more than the barest glimmer of warning, tore apart. Thousands of pieces of jagged metal fluttered toward the earth, sparkling in the sun. Once again, a machine had smashed into the invisible wall in the skies, and once again, a man would never come home.

It happened much too often. Scientists cursed their helplessness as fine young men died. Slowly but surely they identified the enemies. They called them by strange names—creep, flutter, resonance, compressibility. All of them were deadly; defeating them required painstaking labor on the part of the scientists, and raw, naked courage on the part of the pilots.

Slowly, flight by flight, pilot by pilot, the engineers and scientists began to comprehend their problems. And because there were always more pilots to step into the breach left by their dead friends, they whipped the problems.

One of the most bitter lessons that had to be learned in the new realm of flight, not yet twenty years old, was that an airplane flying below the speed of sound can still be affected by the movement of air at supersonic speed.

We learned the hard way—by patiently assembling pieces of smashed and torn aircraft—that sound travels in the form of a shock wave. We knew this to be true of sound traveling freely through the atmosphere. It took more time to learn that the same shock wave, racing across the parts of an airplane, can build up into a wedge; the shock waves pile up into a dangerous, crowding mass of air. An airplane moving through the air forms an image of its flight in the form of a shock wave—a wave of sound. As the airplane approaches the speed of sound, the shock waves are moving barely ahead of the airplane. Soon the two speeds are similar, and the two forces moving through the air, the airplane and its shock waves, begin to crowd one another in the same small portion of sky.

What puzzled engineers most was that the effects of supersonic flight were smashing airplanes that had not yet reached the speed of sound.

The secret lay in the fact that as air curves over a wing or the body of an airplane, it speeds up in its movement. As it starts over the wing, its speed is subsonic. Midway across the wing, it has become a shock wave moving at the speed of sound. At this point it can't get out of its own way. The airplane lacks the power to move any faster. Compressed by the tremendous forces at work, the sound waves begin to pile up. The shock waves of compressibility become diamond-hard razors driven with piston force against the airplane.

The inevitable occurred—the wings snapped in half, fuselages twisted and tore apart, tail sections ripped off. And the sequel to the inevitable was always the same—another obituary to be written.

Slowly, though, we learned enough to probe cautiously but ever faster into the sonic regions. We abandoned the propeller-driven airplane as aerodynamically forbidden to enter the higher compressibility ranges. Even the early jets lacked the finesse of design and the naked power to accomplish flight at supersonic speed. We had no alternative but to turn to a new source of power. This source was the rocket, which was new in the sense that only recently had we begun to harness its energy, to chain its unpredictable explosive nature, to quell its natural tendencies to transform a gleaming fuel tank into a churning, expanding ball of fire and wreckage.

On October 14, 1947, a four-engine bomber climbed into the sky, carrying beneath its belly a small, orange monstrosity of an airplane, the XS-1. Captain Charles Yeager was squeezed uncomfortably into its tiny cockpit; it had a swollen, misshapen body and small, stubby wings. Mounted in its squat, unlovely tail was a rocket motor, an incredibly powerful rocket motor. This above all was its saving grace.

Most pilots would have given high odds that Chuck Yeager would never return in one piece. Six miles over the Mojave Desert, Yeager released the XS-1 from the body of the mother airplane. He flicked on four switches; in response to the movement of his gloved hand, long streamers of dazzling fire gushed rearward from the little airplane. This was naked power.

Within seconds the XS-1 was shaking madly, but from the grip of compressibility, not from the dazzling energy of its rockets. Yeager careened wildly into the reefs, and there could be no mistaking the sawtoothed coral of compressibility that hammered and tossed the XS-1. In the cockpit, all that sustained Yeager's consciousness was the system of webbing and straps that bound his body. Despite this protection the wild buffeting whipped him back and forth like a leaf in a whirlwind. The vibration and shaking, the hammer-like blows, increased in fury until it seemed that neither man nor machine could endure any longer.

Then suddenly, miraculously, there came a moment of relief—a moment that lasted. The little airplane was through; it had crossed the barrier. It sailed on, spewing flame and diamond-shaped shock waves in its wake, cruising just beyond the reefs.

Now Yeager flicked the switches off, rode the buffeting back on down through the barrier, and sailed home in a powerless glide to settle smoothly to the dry lakebed just outside Edwards Air Force Base.

If we are searching for milestones by which to measure man's progress toward the moon, this is as meaningful a date as any. Yeager's precedent-shattering flight did not close the book on the problems of compressibility and shock waves. But it did prove that, to a certain distance of penetration, we could cross the barrier reefs and lunge onward. But only to a certain distance.

In the years that followed, these forays into the reefs demanded further sacrifice. Six years after he first cracked through the sound barrier, Yeager found himself once again in the claws of the compressibility demon. But whatever had transpired before, it was a pleasant sail on a sunny afternoon compared to the pummeling he absorbed in December of 1953. Hunched tightly in the cockpit of the new X-1A, Yeager thundered on to more than 70,000 feet and the little X-1A burst to a speed of nearly 1,700 miles per hour.

Then the tiny craft went berserk. In the long seconds that followed, Chuck Yeager was assailed by forces unknown and undreamed of by any other pilot. The little rocket airplane broke from her forward flight into a screaming yaw and hurled herself almost sideways through the air. At a speed greater than two and a half times the speed of sound, the effect was catastrophic. The almost-solid metal wings, stronger even than those on the original airplane, twisted and flexed madly as though made of rubber. Before Yeager's horrified eyes, they twisted and vibrated, rippling along their entire span. By every sliderule measure, those wings should have ripped away from the fuselage.

But they didn't, and Yeager was committed to his insane plunge down through the sky. The X-1A pitched nose up and down in violent movements, yawing and skidding, a creature gone mad.

From the wingtips there streamed gray and gleaming banners of light. Sharply defined as knife edges, they ghosted into existence before Yeager's astonished gaze. Then other banners came into view, broader and thicker, even more brilliant: glowing blades of light that spread backward at different angles from the airplane's sharp prow to intersect with those sailing back from the wings.

They increased their intensity, ebbed, and returned almost instantly, impossibly sharp and crystalline. They were bands of light. *Shock waves.* That was enough for Yeager. He flicked off the power switches.

He was an instant too late. A motor tube sputtered. The rearward thrust from the rockets was uneven. Catastrophe compounded itself—and Yeager found himself totally and completely helpless as a mountain swooped out of nowhere and smashed the X-1A wildly through the skies. Then, as Yeager's heart pounded wildly, she slewed crazily about and stood on her left wing. From that instant on, Yeager was a rag doll beaten and pummeled as though steel fists rained blows upon his body.

The airplane swooped up and over in an impossible parabola through the skies—never, not for an instant, ceasing its uncontrolled, maddening antics. She whipped over on her back and spun with terrifying speed. With bone-wrenching force the spin ended, only to be replaced with a fearful cartwheeling through the edge of space.

We have become familiar with the terms "acceleration" and "deceleration" through the press coverage on our astronauts. But this was as nothing compared to the mauling Yeager received inside that screaming, madly gyrating machine! At one moment Yeager's body sagged like a crushed rag doll beneath the battering ram of plus-gravity forces. In the next instant, the maddened whirling of the X-1A reversed the direction of the force, sending through Yeager's body the knives of pain from many times normal weight in one direction—to that same force changing almost instantly to the other direction.

Yeager went through the worst torments of acceleration gone insane. It is bad enough when a man in the cockpit of a fighter airplane must endure a *fluid shift*—the movement of blood and body fluids downward toward his lower extremities—and the force keeps these liquids there, distending tissues and veins. But no words can ever convey the punishment when the blood sloshes back and forth with the weight of mercury, squeezing and bloating and distending in mad rushes through the organs. Out of a moment when the blood drained away from his head, when grayness swept into his vision and the world reeled, there came a blinding red flash in his eyes. The red was blood pounding into Yeager's eyes and brain, swelling the veins, making his eyes bulge.

Through all this, a thousand times more punishment than any man in space has ever endured, Yeager survived. As a test pilot he was a superb physical specimen. He drew strength from experience, from training and from the determination that brought him into this tiny, cramped, pain-filled prison.

He was not entirely without protection. Special harnesses gripped his body. Their clasp upon his skin during the violence of his gyrations left bruises and welts, but they helped to save his life.

Around the lower part of Yeager's body was a close-fitting contraption formed of pressure lines and five bladders. It is called a G-suit, but this is inaccurate. More properly, it is an *anti-G* suit. Under any onslaught of G-forces, the suit immediately inflates. This is automatic. Air rams into the lines under high pressure, rushes to fill the bladders. The bladders in turn squeeze tightly around the stomach, thighs, and legs. They squeeze as tightly as a boa constrictor. They stem the rush of blood, limit the fluid shift, prevent the veins and arteries from distending to the point of rupture.

This was not all he had for protection. About his body he wore an uncomfortable, tight-fitting pressure suit. He also wore a snug, sealed pressure helmet. As the X-1A went berserk, the suit immediately inflated. Pressure on his entire body clasped him in a tight and crushing grip.

Without these aids Yeager would never have survived. Despite the incessant punishment, gasping for breath, stabbed with pain, he not only remained conscious, but struggled throughout his mad flight to regain control of his machine.

Until, suddenly, his body shot straight up. Despite the straps and the harnesses, the movement of the little airplane was so violent that Yeager's helmet crashed against the canopy and cracked the extremely hard inner glass. The severe blow jolted Yeager into unconsciousness. During these moments of complete blackout the X-1A continued its terrifying plunge—a crazy, gyrating, whirling shriek across and down the sky for more than ten miles. Barely twenty thousand feet above the desert, in air now fairly dense, Yeager sensed the return of control into his hands.

Chuck Yeager brought the stub-winged machine—considered a "bastard to land" by every pilot who flew her—down to an unpowered, perfect touchdown on the desert floor.

Yeager, of course, is not the only man to have endured and fought his way back. But without question he is one of the finest examples of the breed of test pilot, and of aeromedical volunteer. These are the men who proved that the safety and well-being of astronauts were assured, that insofar as the human body was concerned, nothing known of the flights into space would compromise the life of these men.

Before the first American went into orbit, the guesswork was far behind us. Test pilots and other volunteers, some of them no longer with us, and distressingly unknown to the public, had "gone the route" before.

Can a man withstand the effects of explosive decompression at an altitude where he will *nearly* die? How high up can he go, be thrust into near-vacuum conditions, and survive?

Dozens of men in pressure chambers donned protective suits, waddled clumsily into the chambers, and sat patiently while the air about them hissed away. When they were at 40,000, 50,000 feet, even higher, they deliberately broke the thin line of protection between their bodies and that partial vacuum.

A great many of them suffered biting pains, and sometimes severe, screaming agony. They bled from their noses and they bled from their mouths. Some of them did it a few hundred times, just to be certain that the men who flew to the edge of space could know, beyond all question, because someone else had tested the equipment personally, that they would be all right if everything went wrong.

There were accidents, too, in the "safety" of these chambers. Some men were hurt—badly. Their insides were all scrambled up. And some of them died.

Still, others shuffled into the chambers. It seems impossible, now that all of it is far behind us, that there were so many, so willing, without extra pay or special dividends or privileges, to chart the course and pave the way with the proof of risking their lives.

How much acceleration can a man withstand? The way to find out is to strap him into a gondola at the end of a giant steel arm attached to a massive powerhouse in the center of a great room.

The man is whirled faster and faster until the blood drains from his eyes and his brain, and his body slumps ever so slightly, and he is unconscious. But his head does not fall limply against his chest because a massive, invisible hand is squeezing him inexorably against the headrest. And finally the doctors signal enough; the machine unwinds and gentle hands lift the prostrate form from the gondola.

And the next day, or perhaps three days or a week later, the same man is back there again, waiting to climb into the torture rack for another go at it.

How much deceleration can the human body withstand? Well, there was one sure way to find out. Men climbed into the same centrifuges that they and other men had ridden for acceleration tests. But now the problem was one of deceleration—of slamming to a stop.

Sometimes, as they reached eight and ten and fifteen times the force of gravity, the straps that held their heads tightly in place failed.

The centrifuges could do only so much, and so the men moved out to the deserts. Here engineers built the finest precision railroad tracks in the world. The engineers placed sleds and platforms on the tracks. These vehicles rode, not on wheels, but on slippers that curved around and gripped the rails. Behind the sleds went batteries of great rockets that screamed howling blasts of flame.

Many men rode these flaming, shrieking rails until the sleds smashed into water barriers and a thousand steel hands gripped the bodies of the men, whipping them forward. Bones were pulled from sockets, thousands of tiny veins broke and bled so that the volunteers sometimes looked like boiled lobsters. They lost their eyesight temporarily.

Of them all, every last one to a man stands aside in deference to a man whom they, and all pilots, call the "bravest man who ever lived." He is John Paul Stapp, Jr., a doctor and an Air Force colonel.

Perhaps the most unusual respect paid Colonel Stapp came from the Soviet cosmonauts, who were provided with every available detail of this man's willing experiments on the wild rockets that screamed down the desert tracks.

Stapp, like his co-workers, made many runs down the tracks. On one sled run John Paul Stapp, Jr., endured a deceleration force of 46.2 times that of normal gravity. Under this kind of deceleration, a 175-pound man weighs more than four tons.

Before this incredible sled run in December 1954, Stapp had made twenty-eight runs on different rocket sleds. One would never guess that he failed to walk away from all these tests, nor that he had suffered a fractured rib, several fractures of his right wrist, several minor brain concussions, a severe hemorrhage in his right eye that left him with a serious blind spot for three days, and on one occasion a blinding headache that tormented him mercilessly for three days and nights. Too, there were many dime-sized blood blisters from grains of sand that knifed into his chest and shoulders.

What did Stapp's terrifying run down the desert track reveal? It proved, of course, that with the proper restraint system a man could withstand the brutal deceleration the doctor endured. It proved also that a man could be ejected from a jet fighter at 40,000 feet even if he were flying at a thousand miles per hour, for this was precisely the same force that slammed into Stapp's body at sea level, where the air is denser.

There were men who slid into mummy-cased containers filled with water, who breathed through tubes and let their bodies be whirled around in a centrifuge with punishing force. Other men remained in cold chambers until they felt as though their bones were frozen solid, while their friends in chambers in buildings across the street were exposed to sustained, brutal heat that numbed the senses.

Men were exploded out of airplanes at high subsonic and at supersonic speeds. Limbs twisted from their sockets, faces cut raw by shrieking winds, they fell slowly toward the earth beneath parachutes, proving that under the worst of all possible circumstances a man could travel to the edge of space—and live. They built a solid foundation of knowledge through test after test, through their own repeated exposure to unbelievable dangers. Many were hurt, some critically. Others could never tell us of their final moments of pain.

Captain Joseph W. Kittinger's mission was simple enough. A man who must abandon his machine at the edge of space, under all present protective systems, is doomed. It is as simple as that. Let us say that a man must eject from a spacecraft that has just rocketed away from an exploding booster. One hundred thousand feet above the earth, there is no atmosphere. All the protective devices of flight necessary to sustain a man at a height of one hundred miles are also necessary at one hundred thousand feet. Even with his pressure suit and other personal equipment, if a man— pilot or astronaut—is forced to leave a stricken machine at this height, it is extremely doubtful if he will survive.

If he has a parachute, he cannot open it. He is in air so thin that it does not act against the parachute canopy. Instead, the great canopy drifts aimlessly, like a feather in a breeze.

When he reaches air sufficiently dense for the parachute to open, he is still moving at such great speed (a man at this height falls much faster than the speed of sound) that the tremendous shock of deceleration will probably crush his body. There is also the danger of friction of the parachute with the shock-wave effect of the opening—a blow that can tear the panels out of the chute or even flashburn it, condemning the man to that long and fatal drop to the earth far below.

Let us assume, then, that the man has successfully opened his parachute. At this height he will have condemned himself to (1) death by freezing before he reaches the ground, because the temperature for most of the way down will be as low as 110 degrees below zero, and (2) death by hypoxia. Long before he reaches the lower and denser air, the man's emergency oxygen supply will be exhausted.

There is an alternative. The man can enter into a sustained free fall. Rather than trying to open his parachute, he will fall freely toward the earth. Far down, the increased density of the air will have slowed his plunge to about 150 miles per hour, and he can safely deploy his chute. The fall will not require so much time that he will freeze or consume all his oxygen.

It is a neat solution to the problem, with only one fault. It doesn't work.

The problem is the almost certain action of the unstabilized human body in so long a plunge. Without dense air against which a man can control his fall—and only the experienced jumper may be expected to do this—the body falls haphazardly. Almost always, just before it reaches its maximum (terminal) velocity, the body whips into a violent flat spin that can and has killed men. This spin is so rapid that the centrifugal force of the movement blacks out the pilot. Within the next few seconds the speed of the spin increases enormously, until the body is rotating at a speed of two hundred revolutions per minute, or even more. That is more than twice the speed necessary to rupture a man's blood vessels and kill him.

With the support of Colonel Stapp, Joseph Kittinger, and a colleague, Francis Beaupre, worked on a new parachute design. The parachute was completely Beaupre's idea, but he will insist that an idea is worthless until it is proven effective—and this was Joe Kittinger's mission.

Essentially, the Beaupre chute featured a small, six-foot stabilization chute that deployed at great altitude, seconds before the body reached its terminal velocity. The stabilization chute slowed the body only slightly, permitting the free fall to be carried out. But it stabilized the man's body, whether he was conscious or not, in that long plunge back to earth.

As part of Project Excelsior, Kittinger made his first jump from 76,400 feet. He rode to this height in an open gondola suspended beneath a balloon. He wore a bulky and uncomfortable modified partial pressure suit. Some fifteen miles above the earth, Joe left the gondola. He was to fall freely for sixteen seconds; then, an automatic timer would release the Beaupre stabilization chute.

Joseph Kittinger is an avid believer in Murphy's First Law of Physics—"What can go wrong will go wrong." Excelsior I proved, almost fatally, the validity of Murphy's Law.

The small parachute deployed prematurely, and pulled out the main chute along with it. In that naked air high above the earth the parachute was useless. Instead of pulling all the way out and deploying properly, it wandered like an idiot thing. It drifted down Kittinger's back, coiled lazily between his legs, and then came out on the other side of his body and wrapped loosely around his neck. But with every passing second his speed of fall increased and the air became denser. Soon the wind became a live thing, tugging at the parachute. Before Kittinger could realize what had happened, the nylon shroud lines and canopy had coiled with terrible force around his neck. Only a thick metal ring forming part of his pressure suit prevented him from strangling to death.

At several hundred miles per hour he fell from the sky until his body was almost at terminal velocity and then whipped into a violent, sickening flat spin. He tried every trick he knew to slow the spin, to deploy his parachute. He never made it. His vision began to gray at the edges. Then he lost peripheral vision. Darkness swept over him and he was battered into unconsciousness.

Strick adherence to Murphy's First Law by Beaupre saved Kittinger's life. At fourteen thousand feet, while he was unconscious, and the spin was increasing, an automatic barometric relay clicked home. The small pilot chute on his chest sprang free. Instantly it twisted from the spin into a gnarled rag. But it was no ordinary pilot chute; Beaupre's foresight had led him to make what proved to be a lifesaving modification. The line connecting the small pilot chute to the main canopy, a line for which Beaupre had used nylon of only one tenth the usual strength, snapped from the rotary forces of the spin. Free of pulling strain, like some incredible, twisted animal uncoiling back into normal shape, the main parachute caught wind in its folds and began to unwind, slowed the spin and jerked Kittinger's unconscious body to a safe speed of descent.

He regained his senses on the way down.

A few months later he again rose from the earth in his open gondola. In the stratosphere, on the way up, the pressure glove on his right hand failed. Within several minutes his hand began to swell dangerously. Circulation almost stopped, it turned an icy, painful white. He never told the doctors on the ground what had happened. They might have stopped the test, especially since this was the hand that he would have to use in an emergency if the primary parachute system failed to operate.

His gondola eased to a halt in its climb at 102,800 feet above the earth. Steam and vapor drifted away from his body. Only the equipment he wore on his back prevented a swift and pain-wracked death.

For eleven minutes he drifted at the edge of space. He stared in wonder at the earth's curving horizon, at the velvety blackness of space about and above him. He looked around, drank in the exquisite beauty, the cold of the alien and hostile world.

He shuffled to the open space on one side of the gondola. It was a lonely, remote moment in time. Later he said that he was convinced he would never return alive. Then, to himself, in the privacy of his heart, he said, "Lord, take care of me now."

At 90,000 feet his body fell toward the earth at a speed of greater than seven hundred miles per hour. Beaupre's small chute released exactly as it was supposed to. And Kittinger fell, for an unbelievable four minutes and thirty-seven seconds, in a sustained, stabilized, fully-controlled free fall.

Three miles above the ground the main parachute came out and deployed with a tremendous, wonderful *Crack!*

He was on his way home, drifting gently toward the earth. He knew—as did Beaupre, and Stapp, and all the others involved in the project—that a man could go to the edge of space, that he could abandon a wrecked or burning craft, and that with only the equipment worn on his back, he could be assured of walking through the front door of his home to his family.

All of this—and much, much more—wrote the second part of the overture to space. It evolved slowly, painfully, sometimes fatally. It was assembled out of the grim determination of a few men, and then an increasing number of men, who were willing to try anything necessary to assure that man could survive in space.

When the first cosmonauts and the first astronauts ventured out of this world of ours, most of the world's people waited fearfully to see if the men who went would survive their ordeals.

Most of the people, but not all.

This group of men did not wonder about the outcome. Because of what they had done, they knew the first of our spacemen would survive. The first orbits of men in space were merely the end of a long and perilous beginning.

CHAPTER *3.*

BY THE ROCKETS' RED GLARE

PERHAPS no one aspect of the Age of Space has received more publicity than the booster rockets employed by the United States and the Soviet Union for sending packages of assorted sizes and weights into orbit about the earth, and outward bound for trips to other planets and orbits about the sun. The power, efficiency, and capabilities of these rockets and the merits of Russian versus American boosters have been the prime bone of contention for our public officials and the press.

No one subject has endured so painstaking and studious an examination, and no one subject has simultaneously been so riddled with inaccuracies, so colored by myths and deliberate fabrications. But it is impossible to grasp the requirements for the space age without first understanding the nature of the role played by these mighty engines of space.

Until the moment is reached when centrifugal force replaces aerodynamic lift and a man thunders into actual orbit about the earth, the key to flight is power. This energy must be contained, packaged, controlled, sustained and directed to transfer a package of specific weight and size from its position of rest on the earth's surface to a height of more than one hundred miles and a velocity of approximately 18,000 miles per hour.

The early moments of developing the power which finally reached proportions sufficient to make flight beyond the atmosphere possible had nothing at all to do with man, or with his aspirations for flight in vacuum.

Our literature is filled with the desires and dreams of early rocket engine experimenters, who gazed into star-filled skies and with choked voices predicted the times when men would wander in among those gleaming pinpoints of light. Unfortunately, there is a deep abyss between such dreams and any meaningful promise of seeing them fulfilled.

In aviation and flight, it is impossible, in the profusion of studies, tests, dreams, attempts and engineering endeavors of many decades past, to point to the exact moment when flight could be said to have left the haziness of a dream and assumed the mantle of a science. There were too many unrelated studies and probings of the mysteries of flight, and the attempts to fathom the secrets of manned flight often proceeded on parallel courses. The definition of the exact moment must necessarily be arbitrary, such as assigning the "beginning of manned flight" to the awkward hop of the Wright Brothers on December 17, 1903. The Wrights would be the first to deny, perhaps with much righteous indignation, that it "started" on December 17th; this was the date that provided a fitting and dramatic climax to their labors and errors, their studies with their revolutionary wind tunnel, their failures and their successes. This was vindication.

There is a problem of similar proportion in identifying the moment when the development of controlled rocket energy was transformed from a dream to the inevitable sending of packages through the vacuum of space.

Contemporary historians are eager to label the "rocket age" as beginning during the period when Germany (during World War II) broke down the technological barriers to the development of true rocket power. The hardware in question is the A-4 rocket, much better known to the world as the V-2, the first self-propelled ballistic missile ever to be employed as a weapon.

The A-4 creators deserve all the plaudits of the scientific world, which had waited with some impatience for the vehicle that could carry their instruments away from the earth. For the A-4 was a true, powerful rocket in every sense of the word.

Compared to the sophisticated giants which both we and our Soviet contemporaries employ for shots into space, the A-4 rocket is an archaic monstrosity. It is a crude, bulky, inefficient, clumsy vehicle. Its propulsion system seems a hundred years old. Its control and guidance systems belong, and are, in museums.

Yet only twenty years ago—indeed, as late as only twelve years ago—it was still the most powerful, useful rocket machine in use. If ever a single vehicle is separated from the growing number of old and discarded rockets, to be afforded the accolade of "ancestor of the spaceship," the German A-4 is that vehicle.

It is true that Dr. Robert H. Goddard, the American rocket scientist pioneer, was internationally recognized as the "father of rocketry." Since he was the first man ever to fire (in 1926) a liquid-fueled rocket vehicle, Dr. Goddard's applications of his knowledge to the rocket vehicles he built and fired for some time knew no peer anywhere in the world. It is sad but true, however, that local authorities hounded Dr. Goddard and drove him to the obscurity of the western desert. The world's leading newspapers ridiculed him as a crackpot. He performed much of his work on a budget which might be kindly described as austere.

It is also true that despite their promise and excellent design, Goddard's rockets never achieved outstanding performance. Without the financial means to create extensive test facilities, without a staff of hundreds or even thousands of people, Goddard's work was doomed from the start to home-made, bench-constructed vehicles. They were the pitiful best that Goddard, from his meager resources, could muster against the powerful A-4 rocket which Germany, under the harsh demands for a devastating "secret weapon," produced by the thousands.

With World War II at an end, the A-4 rocket vanished as a weapon and was replaced by the A-4 rocket as a scientific and engineering tool, and also as the foundation upon which a greater and more efficient rocket technology could be built.

In the years following the end of the War, both the United States and the Soviet Union had a golden opportunity. Each was presented on a platter the fruits of all the German work. Equally important, both the United States and the Soviet Union enjoyed a rich historical heritage in rocketry.

The United States had been the first to fire a liquid-fueled rocket. To a limited extent other men carried on Goddard's work. Their efforts included terrifying the citizens of Staten Island, New York, with shrieking, flaming and invariably uncontrollable rockets. But at their best these were little more than the crude products of men who were forced to work with limited funds and primitive facilities.

The Soviet Union lacked the unprecedented technological stature of the United States, and it had much to do to repair the devastation suffered during the war. But it had something else, something of which few people beyond Russian borders were aware. That was a background in rocketry that, until 1934, was second to none in the world. Only Germany, with her zeal for secret weapons during World War II, had moved ahead of the Russians.

At war's end the scientists came to the United States, plucked from their hiding places in the southern Harz Mountains by the United States Third Army. With them came the bulk, and the absolute best, of German documents, blueprints, wind-tunnel results, and other invaluable papers. As icing on the cake, there were three hundred freight cars crammed with the parts and assemblies of the A-4 rockets.

To the Russians went the less desirable spoils of war. They obtained the production centers of the A-4, but these were valuable only in producing additional rockets for tests, production experience and scientific shots.

The world paid little attention to the differences in quality and quantity of the technological war spoils snatched up by the Russians and the Americans. It was not until years later, with the totally unexpected emergence of the Soviet Union as a towering technological giant, that Americans searched anxiously for the balm with which to salve their badly damaged pride. The result was inevitable. There sprang up a series of myths and fables about the rocket contest between the Russians and the Americans, and the capabilities of each, that has unfortunately clouded the true picture of this vast technological race.

Perhaps the most original of these fables arose out of the attempt by the United States to "save face." This story claimed that the vaunted achievements of the Germans were not of German origin at all, and instead resulted from American leadership in rocket design. It went: "The whole world knows that it was the United States that fired the world's first liquid-fuel rockets. Dr. Goddard was the true pioneer in this field. The Germans stole the results of his work, and that's how they came to forge ahead in building rockets."

It is a neat, logical and utterly childish conclusion.

Dr. Walter R. Dornberger is the Technical Assistant to the President of the Bell Aerospace Corporation. Of particular interest is his previous work as Commandant of the experimental rocket station at Peenemunde during World War II, and also as chief of all rocket development in Berlin. A Congressional Committee, * asked Dr. Dornberger: During the "early developments in Peenemunde . . . did you use the research and experiments of Dr. Goddard to any extent?"

The reply:

* "Astronautics and Space Exploration," Hearings before the Select Committee on Astronautics and Space Exploration, 1958.

No, we did not. Dr. Goddard was almost unknown to us. At least ninety-eight percent of Dr. Goddard's patents were classified. We had no access to them. We had some information about Dr. Goddard's work by the American Rocket Society Journals, and that was all we got. But at that time, when we got knowledge, and we learned about Professor Goddard's achievements, we were already ahead and far ahead of him. The development in Germany was parallel to Dr. Goddard's and not one after the other.

The second fable was that the Russians stormed ahead of the United States in the development of great rockets because they had captured all of the German scientists in Peenemunde. And President Eisenhower contributed most heavily to this fable.

But did the Russians capture any scientists, or technicians, or engineers? Most certainly they did; they swept up hundreds of these technical people. Ah then, could the Russians have gained their distinct superiority in rocket power through the services of these men? The myth is persistent. But Dr. Wernher von Braun put this matter to rest:

> The definite impression I got from these debriefings [of German personnel who had returned from Soviet Russia] was that the Russians had made very poor use of the German scientists they had taken into Soviet Russia and that, by and large, the Russian missile program was pretty confused and poorly administered.
>
> It became clear to me only much later that there existed an entirely independent Soviet Russia ballistic missile development program of which the German scientists taken into Soviet Russia were not even aware.
>
> This also answers a question frequently raised these days, namely, what was the probable contribution of German scientists working in Russia toward the Sputnik program. I think the answer is very little.
>
> ... the German scientists taken into Russia were obviously

not even aware of the large and extensive ballistic missile program that was going on inside Soviet Russia. From what we could gather from these debriefing reports, the German scientists were merely squeezed out; they were asked questions like, "How did you do this, and how did you do that?"

They were frequently requested to explain German reports from the Peenemunde archives that had been taken to Soviet Russia. They had to piece old equipment together, and they made lots of design and feasibility studies on paper. But they did not to any appreciable extent actively participate in the hardware phases of the rocket and missile development program in Soviet Russia.

... I believe the Russians made extensive use of the German progress in rocket technology during the last war and whatever they learned from German scientific reports taken into Russia as war booty. But on this foundation they built their own program with their own people.

The Sputniks are definitely the result of a Russian program with little if any assistance.

The activities of the Soviet Union in the field of espionage have been extensively described and documented. Soviet procurement through every method possible of the details of our nuclear programs aided the Russians to an unknown but considerable extent in the development of their own nuclear weaponry. Soviet inferiority in the design and use of large bomber and transport aircraft led them in 1945 to impound and spirit away to the Russian homeland American B-29 bombers that landed on Soviet soil during World War II. The unabashed willingness of the Russians to leapfrog the deficiencies in their technological structure could hardly be concealed, when exact copies of those same B-29s later appeared in large number in Russian skies.

Thus, it seemed almost natural to assume, when the first Sputniks raced into the heavens, that the Russians by themselves could not possibly have created the great rockets for these feats. It seemed natural, and it was desirable, to disregard the lesson of life that what applied in all reason to a situation of a decade past need not necessarily remain valid for the present.

The immediate reaction on the part of many people was generally to place the credit for Russian rocket progress in the lap of the Germans. But there were many other Americans, including some men who "reported" on the news and who wrote patriotic editorials, who refused to afford credit to anyone for anything— unless, of course, they were Americans.

Pointing with indignation to the Soviet record of espionage in the nuclear and aircraft fields, these defenders of American technological virtue waxed eloquent to the effect that the Russians were still busy in their acts of espionage. This latter conclusion could not be denied, but reality begat myth when the editorial writers sped on to the conclusion that "the Russians are in space *because they stole our rocket secrets!*"

The matter may be resolved with a question:

"If the Russians did indeed steal our rocket secrets, why did we not keep a carbon copy?"

What emerges most clearly is that the Russian development of powerful rockets is an effort indigenous to Russian science and technology. It is a result of realistic understanding of the role which the powerful, accurate, long-range rocket was to play in the international affairs of the world's two greatest powers.

Almost as quickly as it passed into history, the Russians, in their patently realistic approach to the needs of the USSR, dismissed the vast effort that World War II represented. The War was finished.

In the late 1940's the Russians looked hard and long at the ballistic missile. Its capabilities were clear. Serious problems in development were apparent, but there could be no question that in the immediate future the rocket would emerge from its crude and erratic beginnings. The result of its development would be a new vehicle of enormous power. This meant the ability to rush in a ballistic arc from one point of the earth to another point as much as ten thousand miles distant.

If there were energy enough contained within that rocket, it could do much more than simply explode out of the atmosphere and fall back to earth almost halfway around the world. In performing this feat, it could carry a heavy weight—weight in the form of a nuclear warhead. The Russians did not doubt that the rocket not yet built, but which they could build, would accomplish what they demanded of it. Yet this was only two thirds of the necessary rocket. Could this same ballistic vehicle, with its ponderous warhead, be directed with accuracy toward some distant target?

This one requirement overshadowed all others. Accuracy, dictated by electronic means and assured by mechanical reliability and response, was the weak link in the chain. Such accuracy could be achieved only with an advanced technology superbly skilled in the mathematical sciences.

Could the USSR undertake such a feat with any promise of success? Not for a moment did the Soviets doubt that this lay within their powers. The scientists established a plan. It was simple and yet took extraordinary advantage of the capabilities of the Soviet Union.

The scientists met with the political leaders of the USSR. The needs of the country were explicit. To properly utilize the destructive force of the nuclear warhead, it must be delivered over intercontinental distances. Its delivery must be swift so as to overwhelm the defensive capabilities of the enemy. The new weapon—the Intercontinental Ballistic Missile—was to be a weapon not only of space, but of *time*.

It was all very simple. If one nation possessed a number of such vehicles, and supported these weapons with the organization and the means to apply them against an enemy who lacked the same striking capacity, this one nation might attain a position of overwhelming military superiority.

Black and white. No grays, no shadows. The government called in its industrial and military specialists and detailed the nation's requirements. The engineers, the military leaders, and the scientists—fully supported by the political leaders—drew up their plans and made known their requirements. The Kremlin assured them that these requirements would be met.

And so the USSR plunged headlong into the future.

The road was long and unbelievably difficult. Much of the country lay prostrate. But the Russians had a goal in mind. They worked by day and they worked by night. And they were extraordinarily skilled in their labors.

In March 1960, before a Congressional Committee, Vice Admiral John T. Hayward, USN, Assistant Chief of Naval Operations for Research and Development, struck an unhappy note which should have been sounded clarion-clear many years before. The Admiral stated the facts flatly: "They [the Russians] are probably the best pure mathematicians in the world. They probably do more work with nonlinear equations than any of our designers do. They do have some fields that they are ahead otherwise, other than the thrust."

The Russians built the rockets, they tested them, and they achieved unbelievable accuracy in their fiery tests out of the atmosphere and, thousands of miles distant, back down again. Every time the thunder from one of these great boosters echoed across the remote lands of the Soviet Union, a new age rushed closer and closer.

Did this activity go unnoticed? It may have been ignored, but it was not unnoticed.

Evidence that it was not is contained in a special report titled "AIRPOWER," dated February 20, 1957, of the Committee on Armed Services, United States Senate:

The Soviets are rapidly closing the qualitative gap. Yet, our qualitative lead is now being given as justification for our having passed over to the Soviets quantitative superiority in military airpower.

The duplicating approach characteristic of many research and development programs in the Department of Defense, along with the dollar limitations established for such programs, has retarded needed modernization of weapons systems.

These policies have retarded important scientific breakthroughs. They contrast with Soviet policies which have produced extraordinary Soviet progress in the research and development field.

The Soviets exceed the United States in rate of technological development, in training facilities, in speed and quantity of prototype development, in the training of scientists and engineers, and in many other phases of airpower development.

The Department of Defense has permitted duplication, even triplication, among the three services in the development and production of missiles; and has permitted comparable waste in the allocation to the three services of responsibility in the missile field.

The Department of Defense also delayed in giving overriding priority to the ballistic-missile program. As a result, there has been a serious loss of time as compared with the rapid progress of the Soviets in this field.

How could this be possible?

Admiral Hyman Rickover, USN, provided the answer to an absorbed Congressional Committee [on February 3, 1960]:

> In essence, the contest is really between two different systems of administration, between two different bureaucracies. If we place the issue on that basis, if we stop talking about a contest between democracy and totalitarianism, we can get at the root of the problem and find out why their rate of progress is greater than ours, why they are getting ahead of us. In Russia only the most determined and the most competent people can get the best jobs. If they do not do the job, if they botch a job, they are fired, and if they are fired, they

do not have a private company to go to for a job. The Russians do not exercise too much favoritism, either. One of Khrushchev's closest friends was recently removed from the Presidium because he had not done a good job. He did not even get a letter from Khrushchev saying how much he regretted his leaving. He was just told to go. They have the advantage of speed in decision making, the ability to concentrate on a few definite national objectives, to which they apply the necessary energy and resources. They decide what is important technically and industrially, what is important for the political and military power of the state. These items they give national priority. They place a man in charge of a project, they hold him responsible, and they let him alone. If he fails, they get rid of him. They do not hound him day after day and literally prevent him from doing his work, which is the way we treat the men in charge of our large-scale government projects. This way of doing business we can no longer afford.

Thus, the Russians burst through all the tangled undergrowth of technological anemia, of industrial want, of the physical devastation of war. They set themselves a goal, and they overcame their deficiencies with a technological-industrial-scientific team. They built the rockets, and into those rockets they built thrust such as our own nation has yet to match. They created guidance systems second to none in the world. They built something else, too, a level of reliability and dependability for which our engineers ached, but waited many years to achieve.

If we were to be perfectly honest about it all—harshly honest—they were running in a race which we, as a nation, had ignored.

The Russians have rockets more powerful than we do because they started on their development program earlier. Right after World War II, the Russians began work on rockets to carry their nuclear warheads. In those days the warheads were big and heavy, so they needed big rockets. The United States, on the other hand, didn't start to build large rockets until we had whipped the war-head problem. After the big breakthrough in cutting down the size of the nuclear warhead, we began our program to develop the long-range ballistic missile. This is why the Russian rockets are more powerful than ours. They began their work on the large ballistic missile five to eight years before the United States did.

The foregoing adequately summarizes the statements of many people who attempt to explain the disparity of power between American and Soviet rockets. It covers, essentially, the reasoning behind the critical failure of the United States to match or surpass the Soviet Union in lofting heavy packages along ICBM trajectories or, for that matter, into orbit about the earth.

It is this line of explanation that more than any other has cloaked in confusion and fable the whole area of the rocket power of the United States in its competition with the USSR.

In March 1960, Dr. T. Keith Glennan, then Administrator of the National Aeronautics and Space Administration (NASA), presented to the Senate * his official statement on this subject. It is as thorough and representative an explanation as anyone has provided. Dr. Glennan stated:

> As we informed the Congress a year ago, we are unable, as of the present time, to match our competitor in the weight-lifting capability of launch vehicle systems. The reasons for this situation have been stated many times but may well be summarized again.
>
> As you will remember, in the late 1940's the United States elected to continue and further develop the heavy bomber as the delivery system for nuclear weapons. The Soviet Union, having a different base on which to construct its defense position—no heavy bomber force nor bases from which to stage

* Hearings before the NASA Authorization Subcommittee of the Committee on Aeronautical and Space Sciences, United States Senate, Eighty-sixth Congress, Second Session, Part I.

intercontinental flights—chose to build high-thrust rocket systems for ballistic missiles to perform this same task.

Thus, they gained a five- to six-year head start in the concentrated research and development that ultimately led to the rockets used in their ballistic missile system. Further, at the time they made their decision on the size of their ballistic missile delivery systems they had to base them on the existing state of the art of warhead development—and so chose a larger launching vehicle than was later selected by us.

Our decision to develop rocket-propelled ballistic missile systems was made after nuclear warhead development had proceeded to the point where we could plan on smaller overall systems to deliver the same punch.

While our rockets can carry a warhead to the desired target with accuracy in the same manner as the Soviet rockets can, their more powerful rockets have given them an early lead on attention-catching, spectacular flights in space. . . .

The general tone of this statement is not exclusively Dr. Glennan's. It represents the remarks that have been made by generals and admirals, by presidents and congressmen, by senators and their assistants, by scientists and engineers, by educators and historians. These statements after constant repetition ultimately and inevitably become part-and-parcel of our contemporary history.

Notwithstanding this "overwhelming evidence," the majority of these statements are unsupported by the facts.

Myth No. 1: In the latter 1940's the Soviet Union, because it had *"no heavy bomber force nor bases from which to stage intercontinental flights—chose to build high-thrust rocket systems for ballistic missiles to perform this same task."*

In one respect this statement is accurate—that in the latter 1940's the Soviets "chose to build high-thrust rocket systems for ballistic missiles."

But when it purports to show a clear decision by the Soviets to choose the ballistic missile *instead of* the heavy bomber force, it is grossly in error. The fact is that the Russians did both. The very existence of Soviet heavy bombers reduces the assertion to the hollow premise that it is. The "lead time" for a bomber—time from beginning of design to operational models—is often from seven to ten years. As an example, the ten-engine B-36 bomber was designed before World War II, and did not enter service as an operational weapon until the early 1950's.

In the early and mid-1950's there appeared in the Soviet Union considerable numbers—not single prototypes—of different types of heavy bombers. First came the intercontinental range turboprop bombers, followed shortly by pure-jet bombers only slightly smaller than our own massive B-52 Stratofortress. Most recently on the scene is the new giant, the Bounder, a true behemoth as large if not larger than the B-52—and capable of supersonic flight.

Since the end of World War II, the USSR has engaged in the most intensive development program for large jet aircraft of any country in the world. At first these large jet machines were of inferior quality. In more recent years the Soviets have closed the gap between themselves and the United States, and may in fact have begun to edge ahead.

There is yet another source of proof on this matter, one that may be found here in the United States. Thousands of jet interceptors and their air-launched Genie, Falcon, Sidewinder, Sparrow and other missiles were built at costs of several billions of dollars for only one purpose—to stop Russian bombers from striking American cities. Thousands of ground-to-air missiles and supporting radar nets and operational systems for Nike-Ajax, Nike-Hercules, Bomarc, and others exist (again at a cost of several billion dollars) for a single purpose—to stop the Russian heavy jet bomber fleet.

Myth No. 2: Clearly implied in Dr. Glennan's statement is the decision of the United States "in the late 1940's" to "continue and further develop the heavy bomber as the delivery system for nuclear weapons." This decision—while we elected to ignore the ballistic missile system—gave to the USSR *"a five- to six-year head start in the concentrated research and development that ultimately led to the rockets used in their ballistic missile system."*

This is part of the line of thinking that continues with the iteration that: "Our decision to develop rocket-propelled ballistic missile systems was made after nuclear warhead development had proceeded to the point where we could plan on smaller overall systems to deliver the same punch."

What all this boils down to is the sour grapes conclusion that the Russians have bigger, more powerful rockets than the United States because the Russians in the late 1940's "made a mistake that turned out to be an advantage." The clumsy, crude, inefficient, stumbling Russians had no choice but to build enormous, powerful rockets—or so the story goes.

In some respects, it is true. In others, it is not.

It is not true that the USSR began its program to develop the intercontinental ballistic missile before the United States chose to do so.

It is not true that the USSR worked on the development of powerful rocket engines while the United States elected instead to concentrate on the manned bomber—which allegedly had been "abandoned" by the Soviets.

It is not true that we did not begin our ballistic missile development program until after the "warhead breakthrough" in 1953 that led to powerful but smaller and lighter thermonuclear warheads.

It is conceded that the USSR initiated its long-range ballistic missile development effort during the immediate postwar years, from about 1945 to 1948. This effort encompassed both the missile frame and guidance hardware as well as the propulsion systems.

According to the "historical reports," the United States delayed until 1953 or 1954 its commitment to a similar program. Until this time—the so-called "eight lost years"—we dawdled while the Russians launched.

Obviously, we must come right down to the heart of it. When did the United States begin its own effort to develop the long-range ballistic missile?

The answer, strangely enough, is: only six weeks after the formal surrender of the Empire of Japan. On October 31, 1945, the Air Technical Service Command of the Army Air Force laid down specifications to industry for proposals in a new missile research and development effort. A series of missile types and projects were contemplated. Clearly delineated in the series was the requirement for a program to develop a ballistic missile with a range of 5,000 miles.

The Convair organization of California (now the Astronautics Division of General Dynamics) submitted to the AAF on January 10, 1946, its formal proposal for a ballistic missile of intercontinental range, and three months later received a $1,400,000 contract for a study and development program. In June 1946 the AAF added another half-million dollars to the original contract with the request that the Convair activities "be accelerated."

Under a financially austere program, Convair was authorized by the AAF to build and test ten rockets under field conditions to establish the validity of new design concepts for the ballistic weapon that would range five thousand miles. Then, as a preview of the serpentine course our rocket development would follow in the years to come, the AAF—only six weeks after pressing Convair to accelerate the program—stated that funds already assigned would have to stretch out for another year.

The Convair people protested; their protests fell upon the ears of a military service already crippled by the economy axe. Albert E. Lombard, an engineer on the Convair program (called MX-774) stated in May of 1947: "Our project is technically ambitious to a degree that far overshadows the German (V-2) performance. To succeed, I feel that it must receive a backing financially on a scale somewhat of the magnitude of the German activities at Peenemunde. . . ."

The final missile was still in the throes of engineering study. But it began to assume form from the growing number of blueprints and computer-run investigations. The intercontinental ballistic missile would range at least five thousand miles. It would be able to carry an enormous warhead—a package weighing three to four tons—and be lofted with precision into a target a continent away.

Several years later, when the Air Force requested Convair to submit its design with a range increased to 6,325 miles, the company (after working for years with its own funds) not only submitted the engineering details, but built an exact-size wooden mockup of the vehicle.

The missile rose more than ninety feet from the ground. Its fuel tank measured twelve feet in diameter. It would soar at 16,000 miles per hour with its heavy warhead over a range of more than six thousand miles. Five engines pushed the Atlas from the ground, and there were two small vernier engines for precision control and adjustment of final speed.

Thrust of this missile: 750,000 pounds.

Disposition of this missile: *Scrapped.*

American scientists simply did not believe that the ICBM could ever be made to work. Every time engineers tried to push appropriation requests for the ICBM through Washington, the budgetary officials would pale and remember the words of one of the most eminent and respected scientists in the world, Dr. Vannevar Bush, who in 1945 ridiculed the entire concept of the ICBM: "I say technically I don't think anybody in the world knows how to do such a thing, and I feel confident it will not be done for a very long period of time to come . . . I think we can leave that one out of our thinking. I wish the American people would leave that out of their thinking."

In later years, as our original program to develop the ICBM was strangled and finally shoved unceremoniously into a dark closet, how did the promise of the thermonuclear bomb affect the men who would decide, in terms of the ICBM, to build or not to build?

Dr. Robert Oppenheimer spoke for the majority of scientists when he said, "I'm not sure the miserable thing can be built, or that it can be gotten to a target except by oxcart."

In May 1947, Albert Lombard, engineer on the MX-774 project, which was validating the design concepts of the future Atlas ICBM, warned of the finances needed by the program, and re-emphasized its degree of technical skill and ambition.

In July 1947, the Army Air Forces canceled Project MX-774. In 1948, scraping together what funds remained in the program, Convair fired the three MX-774 missiles built to date. The missiles suffered the normal teething problems of a new vehicle. They also proved out completely the concepts which finally did go into the Atlas ICBM.

In the late summer of 1949, someone yanked open the door of the dark closet into which we had dumped our ICBM studies. The reason for this action had come in dramatic form—a towering mushroom cloud high over a testing ground deep within Russia.

Two years later, in 1951, the Air Force established Project MX-1593. Convair stepped up the pace of studies which, until now, it had privately financed. Convair (with the consent of the Air Force) dubbed its new program Atlas.

Unfortunately for Convair and the Air Force, Atlas was still the hulking brute with five engines and a thrust of 750,000 pounds. It was unfortunate because most engineers still did not believe it was possible to build an ICBM that could meet the requirements of range, payload and accuracy.

Another two years later, in fact in 1953, Atlas was still on paper. Secretary of Defense Charles E. Wilson dismissed as utterly ridiculous the idea that a ballistic missile with 750,000 pounds thrust could be built.

Atlas was thrust back into its closet.

That the Russians were already well along on a ballistic missile of even greater thrust was not a factor that Wilson or his staff permitted to enter the picture.

In August 1953, the USSR exploded a thermonuclear bomb. We had done the same thing the previous year, on November 1, 1952. But there was a difference between the two explosions, and it has been called "the difference with a vengeance."

The American explosion was not that of a bomb. It came from a device as big as a two-story house, filled with refrigeration equipment, and weighing more than sixty-five tons.

The Russian explosion was a bomb. It was, in fact, a warhead. The Russians had carried their bomb to high altitude and then exploded their new weapon.

Military scientists in Washington turned chalk-white at the idea of Soviet intercontinental ballistic missiles with thermonuclear warheads. They went back to Secretary of Defense Wilson.

He turned them away again. The Atlas was too big, too cumbersome, too bulky, too complicated, too everything. It would never work.

Surprisingly, many scientists again agreed with him. Trevor Gardner, the special assistant for research and development to the Secretary of the Air Force, agreed that Atlas as it stood could not wisely be accelerated. He explained that it was vital "to bring the job down to a practical extension of science and technology in 1953."

Speaking of this time period, Lieutenant General (then Major General) Bernard A. Schriever, Commander of the Ballistic Missile Division of the Air Research and Development Command, stated: "A contract was awarded to Convair early in 1951 for the development of an ICBM. This was the original Atlas program, on which conservative development policies were followed because of the technical problems still to be solved. By 1953 impending solu-

tion of most of these problems allowed design and initial construction of Atlas vehicles."

Unfortunately, General Schriever's words are contradicted by
the record. "Initial construction of Atlas vehicles" did not take
place in 1953, for it was not until the following year that the
Air Force even decided on its final configuration for Atlas, and received authorization to begin the program.

In March 1954, the Air Force made the decision to "reorient
and accelerate" its ICBM program. Some time later, Convair presented its plans, and its wooden mockup, for the five-engine,
750,000-pound thrust Atlas ICBM.

The proposal was rejected as impractical. In the light of new
developments in warhead technology, Convair "scaled down" the
Atlas to three engines and 360,000 pounds' thrust.

Dr. George B. Kistiakowsky, Professor of Chemistry, Harvard
University, stated in March 1962: *

> ... the reason for recommending the cutting down of the
> weight was a very sound military consideration. We had to
> consider the time element, how long it would take for the
> United States to create an effective ICBM force and it was
> quite clear then that the development time would be very
> much longer if we stayed with the proposal of creating ICBM's
> in the class of three-quarters of a million pounds of thrust,
> whereas if the total thrust were cut down to something like
> 300,000 pounds, then a development time of five to seven
> years appeared reasonable. We had information on what the
> Russians were doing, and it was pretty clear that if the pro-
> gram were to take beyond five to seven years a serious threat
> to the United States would exist. It was these considerations
> which were presented to the Air Force but basically it was the
> time of development as it depended on the size of the missile.

* "Panel on Science and Technology—Fourth Meeting," Hearings before
the Committee on Science and Astronautics, Eighty-seventh Congress, Second
Session.

In late 1954 and early 1955 the Atlas program was moving into Phase Three—detail design and development. This was one of the most critical stages of Atlas evolution, for up to that point the missile existed predominantly on paper and in the minds of a few key persons. The small amount of "hardware" that had been produced, including the propellant-tank section, was intended only for test usage.*

General Schriever had stated that by 1953 "initial construction of Atlas vehicles" had begun. This statement is patently incorrect, for the contract to initiate final development and construction of Atlas components was not awarded to Convair until January 1955. And General Schriever himself explained that: "Test facilities of the size and scope required for the accelerated missile program were virtually nonexistent in 1954. Consequently a large-scale test facility had to be laid down, as well as one for production facilities."

In late 1955 there was not a single test facility for the launching of any Air Force ballistic missile.

The statement was made by the Air Force in 1955 that the ballistic missile program carried the highest priority of any activity within the Air Force. In truth, this priority at its best carried a dubious value, for it remained strictly within the Air Force and was ignored by the vast industrial facilities of the nation.

The nature of the "highest priority" was "a distinctive ballistic missile stamp indicating urgency" which could be rubber-stamped onto papers to denote a priority. "Although carrying no priority in itself," Brigadier General Ben I. Funk, USAF, admitted in astonishing candor, "its psychological effect was highly beneficial."

In other words, the vital ballistic missile program of the United States was forced to resort to psychological gimmicks in an attempt to achieve the priority its directors desired but could not obtain. General Funk added in frankness that "despite the benefit obtained

* John L. Chapman, Convair-Astronautics, 1960.

from conventional priority ratings and distinctive identification of subcontractors' orders, something more finite was needed."

In 1956, the first of the Convair Atlas missiles was taking shape in a sprawling, three-block-long assembly plant in San Diego, California. The need for "something more finite" in the way of a national priority was still absent.

In 1957, the USSR had completed its design work, and was testing the components for its initial boosters for space programs.

Early the same year the Office of Defense Mobilization assigned to the Atlas program its DX rating, the highest industrial priority rating of the United States. It had come some four years after the country allegedly placed the ICBM on a "highest priority" rating.

Several months later Sputniks I and II roared into orbit.

The record, then, stands clear and unclouded. The United States began its program to develop the ballistic missile of intercontinental range in 1945. Aided by the zeal of the engineering and executive groups of Convair, it pushed its early design studies to a highly advanced technical concept of the greatest promise, which the ensuing years proved to be completely valid.

In 1947, because of severe financial restrictions and the general belief held by scientists and officials in government that the ICBM was a weapon not attainable by American technology, the ICBM development effort was scrapped.

In 1949, with the reality of Russian nuclear warheads, the effort revived feebly. It achieved renewed paper status in 1951, and this status received much agitation but little real support with the explosion of a Russian thermonuclear warhead in 1953.

In 1954 the Atlas program began to assume final shape. But a design commitment to an Atlas of 750,000 pounds thrust was ordered abandoned as "impracticable," and a scaled-down rocket of half this power was decided upon.

In 1956 the first Atlas missiles were being assembled on the assembly lines of Convair. In 1957, before a single experimental ICBM had flown in the United States, the Soviet Union launched two space satellites. And the launching vehicles were modifications of long-range ballistic rockets.

That is the record.

There is one final element which we might reasonably define as the engineering and propulsion part of the prelude to sending robots and manned vehicles into the vacuum beyond earth.

The finest rocket frame, the most elaborate guidance and control system, the heaviest and best designed payload that scientists can create—all of these are a useless pile of junk without the means of transferring the entire assembly into orbit.

The means to accomplish this feat is, of course, propulsion. When the Army Air Forces committed Project MX-774 to the construction of ten experimental rockets for flight testing—of which only three flew—propulsion did not present a problem. The old Bell XS-1 rocket research airplane was a stub-winged barrel which received its power from an archaic assembly of four tubes clustered together to create a single rocket engine. Each tube produced 1,500 pounds thrust; together they roared with 6,000 pounds thrust. Not much, but enough to kick the XS-1 through the sound barrier and well beyond, and enough to power the MX-774 rockets to a designed height of one hundred miles.

This is the area which presents the most baffling of all enigmas in the history of rocket development in the United States from 1946 to the present. In the program to create the ICBM, we vacillated between outright disdain for the whole idea to muttering indecision as to what steps we should take after the urgent need for the ICBM became clearly demonstrated.

At no time during this long and unhappy period, however, did we ever want for the power to propel either the huge brute of an Atlas we failed to build, or its slimmed-down successor. We did not want for power for a very clear reason—we had all we needed.

Since 1944 there have been various types of rocket engine programs in the United States. Some with great promise were abandoned in the face of financial shortages and official blindness—to say nothing of outright hostility toward proposals calling for the expensive development of extremely powerful rocket engines.

In 1945, for example, the Aerojet-General Corporation fired solid-propellant rocket motors of 66,000 pounds thrust. One year later, the same company was firing improved motors of 100,000 pounds thrust. It is more than frustrating to imagine our present status in terms of solid-propellant boosters, had we only elected to continue this motor series in development.

Be that as it may, the decision of the United States to spend $700,000,000 on an air-breathing missile handed us on a silver platter rocket engines that, for their time, exceeded in power anything possessed by the Soviet Union.

That missile was the North American SM-64 Navaho, a program first financed in 1946 and supported heavily in succeeding years. Navaho was a sensation for its time and is still sufficiently daring and advanced to equal almost any other aerodynamic effort in existence today.

Essentially, the Navaho missile was a huge, sleek, sweptwing beauty with two enormous ramjet engines. The ramjet is best described as a stovepipe with a hell of a fire blazing inside, hurling back a stream of superheated exhaust gases. And the Navaho ramjets "were the biggest damned stovepipes in the world," in the words of a project engineer.

The SM-64A Navaho model, the one designed as the final weapon, was a giant missile which would streak at a speed of nearly 2,000 miles per hour, riding more than 80,000 feet above the earth, from this continent to any point within the Soviet Union. It was a hell-on-wings piece of hardware that hasn't yet seen its equal.

But the great ramjets of Navaho posed a problem. They wouldn't work while the sleek missile rested on the ground. The Navaho had to be up and moving fast before its ramjets would fire to full capacity. The engineers solved this problem neatly. They built a tremendous slingshot to hurl the Navaho far into the stratosphere at supersonic speed. This initial burst of power provided Navaho with all the speed and altitude it needed to strike out for its distant targets.

The "slingshot" was the world's most powerful rocket booster. Entirely apart from any ballistic missile program, the United States developed in the mid-1950's a liquid-engine rocket booster *with a thrust of 500,000 pounds*.

The booster for SM-64A had three combustion chambers. In their final form they produced a half-million pounds thrust in a single stage. For a long time every major rocket that flew in the United States was lifted from its pad by the direct descendants or modifications of the engines from the Navaho booster.

Five of these combustion chambers provided the power for an Atlas with a thrust of 750,000 pounds. Two of these chambers, with a lighter, less powerful sustainer engine, form the propulsion system of the present Atlas.

One of the Navaho chambers, uprated in power with design improvements and gain in the efficiency of subsystems, is the propulsion system for the Thor missile and the whole line of space boosters based upon the Thor.

One of the Navaho chambers, modified similarly to the engine in the Thor, is the propulsion system for the Jupiter missile. And eight of the Jupiter engines, improved upon once again, provide the 1,500,000 pounds thrust for the first stage of the towering Saturn C-1B booster rocket.

In 1957 the United States canceled the Navaho missile project. In existence at that time was a single booster rocket of a half-million pounds thrust. It could easily have been uprated to three-quarters of a million pounds or even a million.

Nothing of the sort was done.

The most powerful booster in the world was junked.

Dr. H. Guyford Stever of the Massachusetts Institute of Technology, in March 1962, to the Congress: *

> ... we mustn't forget that we fired a 500,000-pound rocket in the mid-1950's on the Navajo booster program and so we in fact had a very large rocket which we then cut out of the program when the Navajo was canceled, so it isn't that we were far behind the USSR in those days. We just didn't at that time see a very great need. . . . all of the considerations were military at that time. We didn't have really any major communication between the relatively small group of space based scientists and our military people at that time.

This is the glaring thread of omission that runs through this chapter. There was the intercontinental ballistic missile and its tribulations in development, and there were the riches of rocket engine propulsion systems available to us throughout the same period. But no major satellite and space programs evolved from this wealth of rocket energy.

With respect to the space programs of the United States— affected as they were by the availability of 100,000-pound-thrust liquid-rocket engines in 1950, and by 500,000-pound-thrust boosters almost two years before Sputnik I—the record books show almost a complete blank.

In this area the United States did not plan for the new era of space. It entered, in fact, by way of the back door.

* "Panel on Science and Technology—Fourth Meeting," Hearings before the Committee on Science and Astronautics, Eighty-seventh Congress, Second Session.

CHAPTER 4.

SPACE WAS A DIRTY WORD

BEFORE Sputnik I focused attention upon the space programs authorized by the United States Government, the activities that had taken place were cloaked by military security, official policy and a fervent desire to stay out of the public spotlight. Anything even remotely connected to space activities was considered scientific heresy, financial irresponsibility, military incompetence and official foolishness. A broad band of reactions, all unfortunately true. Space in the United States was a dirty word.

Dr. Hugh L. Dryden, the Deputy Administrator of NASA, reflected the view of the civilian scientist (in 1958) when he said, "Before Sputnik, if you mentioned the word *space,* your appropriations would be cut for wasting the people's money on foolish things."

Dr. Wernher von Braun, in his appearance early in 1958 before a Congressional Committee, said that Sputnik I "... was a very great achievement, proving to skeptics the truth of what we ... were ridiculed for even talking about a couple of years ago."

Four years previously, a reporter asked Charles E. Wilson, Secretary of Defense, if we were concerned that the Russians might win the race in sending satellites into orbit. Not a man to mince words, Secretary Wilson retorted, "I wouldn't care if they did."

In March 1961, the Committee on Science and Astronautics, Eighty-Seventh Congress, held a series of special hearings on the role of the military in the space field. In that Report, *"Military Astronautics,"* the Committee prepared a special review of the background history of the military in the space field. It is an interesting little document.

There is no precise point at which Department of Defense interest in space-related technology began. Space capability is compounded of much other knowledge—of chemical propellants, ballistics, special materials, rocket-engine design, radar and communications, computers, servomechanisms, nuclear energy, human-factors work, and ground-support equipment, to mention only the most obvious.

Substantial research in missiles began on a significant scale during World War II, but did not reach conclusive status during that war. After Germany's collapse, it was discovered that some of the men associated with the V-2 rocket ballistic effort at Peenemunde were also interested in space flight. This interest was viewed with seriousness by the authorities, because the Germans had a substantial background of experience in rocket engineering.

Despite the interest in space which various Defense officials can trace back many years, only a few men were really committed to exploring these possibilities, and for a long time it was considered not quite respectable to talk in terms of space flight. In the face of these handicaps, some serious studies were conducted. In March 1946, the Army Air Force set up Project Rand, which included among other objectives the study of satellite applications, and on May 12 of that year, Rand filed a report entitled *"Preliminary Design of an Experimental World-Circling Space Ship."* In the years which followed, all three Services conducted experiments with sounding rockets, or began development of various kinds of guided missiles, producing a fallout of scientific and technical knowledge applicable to space programs later. Research in space biology began as early as 1946, and that year the first radar signals were bounced off the moon. Enough competing study contracts on satellites were initiated so that by October 1947, the Committee on Guided Missiles of the Research and Development Board had to be assigned the responsibility of coordinating the work scattered among the three Services.

Virtually no public mention of space research was made until December 29, 1948, when the First Report of the Secretary of Defense made brief mention of the coordination of studies and component research in the manner referred to above.

In the first half of the 1950's there was more and more public discussion by unofficial groups on the prospects for earth satellite vehicles. In official circles, a key meeting was held by a small minority of interested persons on June 25, 1954, which led to a joint Navy and Army plan for Project Orbiter, a small earth satellite launched by a Redstone rocket; in ultimate execution, it resembled the original plan, and became the early Explorer design.

The frequency of Soviet references to its future plans for space travel was stepped up considerably during these same years. International recognition was then given to these possibilities on October 4, 1954, at the meeting of the Special Committee of the International Geophysical Year (IGY). In March 1955, Dr. Waterman of the National Science Foundation went to the White House with a plan to implement the US portion of the IGY satellite experiment. On July 29, 1955, formal announcement was made of such US intentions, with the work to be performed in the Department of Defense, but carried out independently of military missile programs. A day later, the Soviet Union announced that it, too, would launch IGY satellites. On September 9, by recommendation of the Stewart Committee, the Department of Defense agreed to drop Project Orbiter in favor of a new Project Vanguard, with the Navy as executive agent.

When Sputnik I went into orbit, the United States did not have a single major space program based upon the great power of its rocket engines which had been under development for many years. Major space programs based upon such boosters as the 500,000-pound thrust Navaho did not exist—but not because they were not recommended, or even fought for.

They were. And each one in turn was rejected by the officials who sat highest in different echelons of government. There were not just a few proposals or a few dozen, there were literally hundreds of serious, workable, sensible, technically reliable programs. And one by one each failed to run the gamut of official reticence and outright hostility to such efforts.

As Dr. von Braun explained in 1958 to the Congress: ". . . had a satellite crash program been initiated right after the war—I realize then it could not have been done because nobody was then interested in this kind of a thing—but from the purely technical angle I think we could have fired a satellite in 1950, 1951, or 1952, something like that."

The Project Orbiter satellite mentioned briefly in the Congressional Report entitled *"Military Astronautics"* is one of the more clearly defined military-sponsored scientific space programs which failed to get off the ground.

The meeting of June 25, 1954, mentioned in the Report took place in Room 1803 of T-3 Building of the Office of Naval Research in Washington. Present in the room were Dr. Wernher von Braun; Frederick C. Durant, III; Dr. Fred L. Whipple, the Harvard astronomer; David Young, of Aerojet-General Corporation; Dr. Fred Singer, of the Physics Department, University of Maryland; Alexander Satin, Chief Engineer of the Air Branch of the Office of Naval Research; Commander George W. Hoover, Office of Naval Research; and several other US Navy representatives.

The project was simplicity itself. Take the Redstone ballistic missile (started in 1951 as an Army crash project to develop a battlefield weapon, not a space booster, with a range of about 200 miles), add some existing solid-propellant rockets atop the

Redstone for upper stages, and fire a satellite into orbit. It would
be strictly a scientific satellite, designed and built by scientists.

The rockets, the booster and the upper stages, all existed as on-
the-shelf hardware. They could be assembled in what engineers
call a lashup. It would be crude in comparison to a rocket designed
specifically for a satellite booster purpose, but it would work. It
would place the satellite in orbit and at unbelievably low cost.

Project Orbiter moved quickly ahead. The military groups involved provided enthusiastic approval. The Chief of Naval Research
gave his official blessings. General Holger Toftoy of Redstone Ar-
senal and General Lesley Simon, Chief of Army Ordnance, agreed
that Orbiter should receive full support. The only proviso was that
it should not interfere with any missile program. The Navy assigned Commander Hoover as the Project Officer for Orbiter.

This small group sliced through red tape and, with a minimum
staff, went to work. The Navy accepted responsibility for designing, building, and developing the satellite. The Army would modify
the Jupiter-C rocket (a Redstone modified to test nose cones at
ICBM velocities) as the booster. The Varo Manufacturing Company received a contract for the visibility study portion of the satellite effort. The Aerophysics Corporation would develop the final
shape and design of the upper-stage rockets. The Alabama Engineering and Tool Company was authorized to combine the Loki
upper-stage rocket clusters with the booster's guidance system.
And the Naval Research Laboratory began work on a Minitrack
system to track the satellite in orbit.

Does Minitrack have a familiar ring? It should: When the axe
fell on Orbiter, Minitrack became the system to follow and receive
information from the Vanguard satellite in orbit.

While the Project Orbiter team produced steady, satisfying results in their efforts, a group of eminent American scientists were
suffering sore feet as they trudged from office to office in Washington, trying to obtain authorization to build a satellite for the IGY.

It seems unbelievable, but these scientists apparently knew nothing of the Orbiter project already in existence. Even President Eisenhower has stated flatly that until the scientists finally reached his office with their requests for an IGY satellite effort, he knew nothing of any satellite program in the United States. In one of the outstanding examples of the right hand being entirely unaware of the activities of the left hand, the scientists finally scored in their sales pitch to the United States Government. We would build a satellite for the IGY—and the Government announced this decision on July 29, 1955.

Two months later the scientists announced that the new satellite effort would be Project Vanguard. The Navy would be the executive agency, but the whole program would be strictly a civilian-scientific effort. It would cost the United States some ten million dollars.

What happened to Project Orbiter? In unceremonious terms, Orbiter was dumped.

The scientists were jubilant. Engineers warned them that even though we would build twelve satellite launching vehicles, the odds were that only one satellite out of the twelve would ever get into orbit. No one cared about the odds. One satellite in orbit would be a "stunning achievement," was the official word. (The final results: three satellites launched successfully out of thirteen attempts.)

The fate of Project Orbiter was indicative of the Government attitude toward any space project in general. Dr. von Braun testified before the Congress that: "We fired a three stage vehicle, using the Redstone missile as a first stage, for the first time on the 20th of September 1956. It flew over a range of 3,300 miles, with a payload of 84 pounds. Had we replaced the 84-pound payload of this missile by a fourth stage, as we did later on with the Explorers, this same missile would have been able to orbit."

If the rocket existed and could be put into orbit by the simple expedient of firing the booster, why didn't this happen? An astonished Congressman asked von Braun: "Is it a fact that at the time there was so much pressure to be certain you did not put that instrument in orbit that people came down to see to it that certain parts of it were not activated; is that correct?"

"Yes, sir. . . . Specifically, we were not permitted to fire into orbit."

So it was not just a matter of official blindness, after all. The policy of the United States Government dictated direct intervention with an existing satellite program, with the specific order that no orbital attempt must be made.

This was in 1956—more than one year before Sputnik I.

The scientific community of the United States has on a number of occasions seriously taken to task the military structure that sponsors, aids, and finances basic scientific research. This is one of the more puzzling asides to the monumental confusion and bureaucracy that strangled this country's efforts to launch space programs.

After finally receiving the authorization for an IGY satellite, which became Project Vanguard, the scientific community did *not* as a group wax enthusiastic about the program. When the Government announced a financing of ten million dollars for Vanguard, there arose a hue and cry within scientific circles questioning the wisdom of so great an expenditure. Many scientists disputed openly that any worthwhile gains could come from a satellite of this type, and that the value of the return in scientific information would be the merest fraction of the tremendous sum of money involved.

Remarkably, the scientific community had for years remained conspicuously absent from the proposals to orbit scientific satellites. In many instances our most eminent scientists spoke of satellite proposals as "utter bilge," and clearly dissociated themselves from any such recommendations.

Space was a dirty word.

Early in 1958, General Austin W. Betts, Military Executive Assistant to the Director of Guided Missiles, Department of Defense, explained some of Vanguard's difficulties: ". . . we are now in the

process of putting up $110 million to do what was originally pro-
posed. I say categorically if $110 million had been tied to that
effort as the original price tag, I doubt if it would have obtained
sufficient overall support from the Department of Defense or the
Congress to do it at all."

But Vanguard had been officially recommended and sponsored
by the National Academy of Science, the National Science Foundation, and the United States National Committee for the IGY.

After the President approved Vanguard (for one hundred million dollars *less* than was finally spent), what happened to this
national effort? How did the satellite project, with all its official
enthusiasm on the part of the nation's most eminent scientific institutions, fare in the national picture?

The Director of this combined civilian and scientific space effort, Dr. John P. Hagen, explained in 1958 to a Congressional
Committee that Vanguard is a "major national and international
commitment" that, unfortunately, was seriously hampered by:

> (1) Too low a priority in the overall scheme, (2) virtually
> no industrial priority, (3) piecemeal funding which caused a
> lot of waste motion and cast a pall over the technical area,
> (4) too many administrative channels and levels to go through
> in order to get policy decisions and funds in the time limits
> with which we were dealing.
>
> ... as an index of the state of our planning, Project Van-
> guard has been given no go-ahead of funds for a continuing
> program past the end of this year. We have forwarded very
> comprehensive plans to higher authority over the past six
> months ... Vanguard ... is a national asset which should not
> be allowed to waste a day. ...
>
> [Dr. Hagen stressed that there was a gulf] which exists
> between scientists doing roughly the same work at gross dif-
> ferences in salary, with the civil service classified employee
> always at the bottom of the heap. For instance, the top five
> men on the Vanguard staff, all of whom bear extremely heavy

responsibilities, are classified employees who average about $12,000 a year. Similar responsibilities in industries rate from thirty to 100 percent more in salary. . . .

Dr. Fred L. Whipple, Director of the Smithsonian Astrophysical Laboratory at Cambridge, Massachusetts, before the Congressional Committee (1958), gave inside explanations of extreme-altitude research with sounding rockets. What he had to say raised some of the Congressmen upright in their seats:

> . . . in discussing problems of such fundamental data as the density of the high atmosphere within the rocket range, the Russian scientists with whom we have talked during the past year have seen our published data and only recently have presented their own material.
>
> I saw the results of theirs last fall for the first time at the meeting of the "International Geophysical Year" here in Washington.
>
> The interesting point is that the Russians were not taking our results about the upper atmosphere and utilizing them directly as fact. They were highly critical of our results, and, in fact, said they were not so good. They considered theirs better than ours in spite of the fact that we have had an extremely good upper atmosphere research rocket program carried on by extremely competent people. . . . This sort of information is of great value to other scientists and it is very doubtful, in terms of basic research, that we are going to be much ahead of the USSR in any zone.

To this Dr. Whipple added the conclusion that the high-altitude sounding rocket program faced a dead-end at the end of the IGY, except for some continuing military research work.

The following year, in 1959, the Select Committee on Astronautics and Space Exploration requested of George S. Trimble, Jr., the Vice-President for Engineering of The Martin Company, his conclusions on the state of the space program, and his forecasts of what lay ahead. Mr. Trimble's response deserves close attention:

The answer to the question: "Whither the Space Age in the next decade?" must be considered in two parts. The first is "What *can* we do" and the second is "What *will* we do." Part 1 is the easier of the two to answer because it is a technical question which will submit to measurement and extrapolation of the scientific and economic disciplines. Unfortunately, the answer is academic. The answer to part 2 is the one we really want, but unfortunately it is impossible to acquire with any degree of accuracy because implicit in the question is the human equation—the American public.

To my knowledge no one has been able to predict, to any reliable degree, the behavior pattern of the American public over a ten-year span even for very simple factors such as population growth or movement, and before we can answer the question "What will we do," we must determine what the American people want to do, and perhaps more important, why they want to do it. This is the way our country operates, and it is good.

We must recognize that the present [1959] desire of the American people to "do something" about space is based totally on their feeling of frustration resulting from losing a race they didn't know they were in—launching Earth's first manmade satellite. The people are reacting to a condition set up by Russia, not acting in their own behalf for their own private reasons. Hence, to get a true answer to our question, I must first predict what Russia will do in the Space Age during the next decade; so that I know what the American people will want to do (how they will react); so that I can determine what the technically capable people will be permitted to do; so that I can judge what will actually happen. This certainly seems to me to be an unfruitful pursuit, and particularly for one eminently unqualified to predict the American public, much less the Russian Government.

Based on this question alone, the best tentative answer I could give now to the question "What *will* we do in the Space Age during the next decade?" would be "Considerably less than we are technically and economically capable of doing, and somewhat less than the Russians." This answer is as objective as I know how to make it. Perhaps it is too objective. Perhaps it does not leave enough room for American flexibility. It is but an extrapolation of my observations that groups who are motivated only by reaction to other groups never do their best work and rarely meet the competition. Those who dare to lead and have a reason for it usually lead. . . .

We in this industry and our friends, the customers, agree quite well on what *can* be done. We may argue about details such as how to do it or who should do it, but, as I have already stated, things scientific and technological are not difficult to predict, and so we find agreement amongst men schooled in the subject. But to believe that what *can* be done *will* be done is to be unrealistic. Perhaps a few examples will clarify my position.

Almost 12 years ago a group of people with whom I was associated designed a large vehicle capable of orbiting the Earth. We used the materials and knowledge that were available to us. With the clarity of hindsight, it can now be said that the machine would have worked well, that the Space Age would have been ushered in five to six years earlier and by a different people—by people of the United States of America. My group wasn't the only one with a workable design in 1947. There were several. None of us went ahead with the job because the American people decided not to. We did not know how to sell it to them.

Eighteen months ago, three months before Sputnik I, some of my colleagues and I were laughed out of a very scientific meeting for proposing and showing how to build a large military base on the Moon, not because the people at the meeting disagreed with the feasibility of or desire for the scheme, but because the task of selling the need to the American public seemed so impossible to them that consideration of the proposal seemed a complete waste of time. The scientists apparently did not believe the American people would find any sense in such an idea. I cannot agree with this. . . .

The attainment of knowledge about our environment has been the major human pursuit for at least 600,000 years. It is the essence of civilization and society. The next big step to take in this pursuit is the exploration and exploitation of space. This step is inevitable. The question is who will contribute the most.

Is it not interesting that this job cannot possibly be accomplished by a few men with a single purpose, such as Columbus and the people who financed that trip must have had. To get the job done we must have an enormous number of human beings, all with the same desire, because the job is so large. Here is a challenge greater than any that has been laid before any people in the past. And the hero of this age will not be the space traveler, but rather the man or men who successfully figure out how to motivate 170 million American people actively to do battle with a part of their environment that they just began to hear about, that they really did not know was important—Space.

One need only read a scientific evaluation today of our space program—a multi-billion-dollar effort every year that still bursts its budgetary bonds with each successive fiscal review—to be swept up by the eloquent statements of our scientists about the wonderful things we are doing for ourselves, and for mankind.

Today our scientists appear before the Committees and Panels of the Congress to obtain huge sums of money to finance their projects in space. Without such projects, they warn sternly, the United States will forfeit to the Soviet Union the technological and scientific leadership for the future. It is all true. But where were these same scientists before Sputnik I? They remained, the majority of them, hidden securely from the public spotlight that ridiculed the adherents of projects in space. The price—abuse and ridicule from their own closely knit community—was apparently too high to pay. Space was not a subject to drag out before the public, or before those who directed the budget.

The military wanted space programs—and they were abused. The civilian heads of the agencies of defense left little unsaid in their denunciations of the military, who fought to obtain the authorization to use existing funds and hardware for space projects.

It is impossible to forget the long and bitter struggle waged by engineers and scientists in uniform to obtain some semblance of a program in space. During those long and lean years of such efforts —when more than one career officer put that career on the line, and lost—the scientists almost to a man condemned these same military people as the "untouchables of Washington."

How many plans were thrown unceremoniously into wastebaskets? How many of these military scientists cooled their heels in anterooms, waiting day after day simply to receive a hearing for their programs? How many brilliant, practicable, necessary projects to extend the scientific, technological and military capacities of this country into space were halted in their tracks and the officers muzzled under the cloak of "security"?

In a sense, we might say that the United States presented a huge scientific-political boycott of the future.

Dr. Arthur Kantrowitz, Director of the Avco Research Laboratory of Everett, Massachusetts, was one of those lonely few who tried to push the nation into tomorrow. To a hushed and attentive Congressional Committee, Dr. Kantrowitz in 1958 recommended that the Committee:

> Consider . . . the way that our current administrative decisions concerning great projects are made up by scientific advisory committees made up of distinguished scientists. The membership of these committees cannot, remembering their judicial role, emphasize individuals who have an enthusiasm for the project in question. They, therefore, in their objectivity, record merely the general climate of thinking at the mo-

ment and tend to recommend the adoption of unadventurous
policies.

The "adoption of unadventurous policies" is an art worn smooth
by the less imaginative of our scientific community. Early in 1958,
Rear Admiral John T. Hayward, Assistant Chief of Naval Operations for Research and Development, appeared as a witness before the Congress during hearings on astronautics and space exploration. The Committee selected Admiral Hayward to respond
to a charge made against military space programs in general by a
group of physicists. This group submitted a report detailing what
they thought were the weaknesses in the American missile and
space research programs. The report read:

> Recent startling developments have pointed out for all the
> world to see that we have fallen dangerously behind the
> Soviet Union in the development and exploitation of science
> in the natural interests. This hard fact was not surprising to
> any one who has followed recent trends in the support and
> encouragement of Soviet science, including education, as op-
> posed to our reluctance to place the proper emphasis on intel-
> lectual endeavors. Indeed the past few years have seen the
> emergence of an anti-intellectual climate and an atmosphere
> of smug self-satisfaction which places a premium on con-
> formity and finds us woefully unprepared to meet the current
> challenge.
>
> The root of the difficulties in which we find ourselves is the
> system that places the military in such close control of scien-
> tific research and development.

Admiral Hayward's reply should be required reading for every
American citizen:

> I will answer that by saying I do not know whether any-
> body on this committee can answer the question as to who was
> the first American Nobel Prize winner in physics. I wonder
> if they know? Do you know who he was?

(The unanimous response: *No.*)

He was a naval officer. Michaelson was his name. He made the first measurements of the velocity of light. The National Academy of Science was founded in the United States at the insistence of the Navy. We had people all the way back to Bushnell who made the first submarine. You had my friend, Admiral Rickover, before you this morning.

Well, let me tell you my own history. I started in the Navy as a sailor. I did not graduate from high school. And I won the Life-Saving Medal, and President Coolidge appointed me to the Naval Academy.

Since graduating from the Naval Academy, I studied three years of theoretical physics, specializing in the Einstein theory at the University of Pennsylvania. I went to the University of New Mexico. I went to the California Institute of Technology. I went to Stanford. I went to the University of California.

I worked with Doctor Lauritson in the first [solid] propellant rockets. I worked for Doctor Oppenheimer. I was head of weapons research in the Military Applications Division of the Atomic Energy Commission.

I am not unusual in any way. We have very many military people who are very competent scientists. I am convinced in my own mind. And I am sure—General Groves would agree with me—that we would not have had an atomic weapon today if it had not been for people like the late Admiral Parsons. . . . The Office of Naval Research was established in 1946 to fill the gap when the Office of Scientific Research and Development was closed after the war, and [it] has given over fifty percent, or contributed money that is involved in over fifty percent, of the doctorates granted in the physical sciences in the United States of America since the end of World War II.

So, when they try and throw the cloak and say military is opposed to science and that we throttle research and development, I object very strenuously.

To add to Admiral Hayward's remarks, where were these scientists in the mid-1950's when the Air Force failed to convince

the scientific authorities of the Government that we should utilize
our powerful rocket boosters such as the 500,000-pound-thrust
Navaho for space missions? Where were they until the day that
Sputnik I rammed the existence of the "new" Soviet Russia into
our everyday reality and suddenly space was no longer something
"to hide beneath the table"?

CHAPTER **5.**

PLUMBING THE DEPTHS OF SPACE

THE scientific investigation of space has produced, among many things, a reiteration of an old principle: The more you know, the more you realize how little you know.

Before we began the firing of satellites to great distances above this planet, we basked in our convictions of the nature of space. It was a big, empty nothing. Light moved through space, in the dim reaches between the galaxies there was dust drifting among the stars, and we knew that gravity exerted its invisible but meaningful play among the celestial bodies and formations. But space itself, the void between worlds, was essentially just a big nothing.

We've changed our opinion. Space is still empty and starkly irreconcilable with man's ability to live. Nature designed man, however, without the means of detecting many of the forces that shape his environment and dictate the patterns of his life. In terms of ferreting out the true nature of events in space, man has been described as a "lout with impaired hearing, critical myopia, thick skin, and a dull brain."

As a part of our space program we have sent scientific packages to whirl and loop for great distances around the earth; we have sent them past the moon and into wide orbits that eventually bring them into their own paths about the sun. These vehicles have employed their electronic sensors to sniff and probe at helium zones, to track down a comet-like tail of gas that may be pursuing the earth like some shadowy creature, to gauge the intensity of particles packing tremendous energy as they rush to the earth from some unknown stellar origin. With astonishment we have noted the effect of light itself on our space chariots, as the enormous and once smooth spherical shape of the Echo balloon satellite pulsated through hundreds of miles in changing its orbit about the earth.

We have found the earth to be encircled by a bewildering variety of zones and belts and rings of radiation. Our sensors have snuffled at the vacuum of space and uncovered the untidiness of our solar system in its flotsam of dust and molecules and other particles. We have measured pressures and temperatures and counted the pinging impact of meteoric particles on shiny metal surfaces.

We have begun to use the medium of space by measuring not only radiations, but also the effect and feel of gravitational and electromagnetic forces. Our satellites have discovered previously unknown "bulges" in the planetary girth of our world, and children in school today talk wonderingly of a "pear-shaped earth"— although the planet is still more perfectly spherical than it is anything else.

It is one thing to talk about numbers of satellites and the struggle to reach out into space, and something entirely different to understand the reason for the struggle. Spending twenty million dollars on a single rocket firing, with only one chance in three of success, simply to determine the density of dust and other particles at a height of two hundred miles, hardly seems an economical venture. It is even more puzzling to the taxpayer, who wonders why that information is required in the first place.

What have we been doing with our satellites? Where have the billions of dollars gone? It is not enough to provide the taxpayer with lists that show satellites launched, satellites orbited, and how one or more particular space shots have told us the temperature of interplanetary gas. The argument boils down to another question: What have we done with what we have learned?

To supply an answer, it is necessary first to understand that there are different types of shots into space. Earth satellites form a variety of experiments and represent an even greater variety of purposes. For example, satellites like the Explorer series, Vanguard, Ariel, Pioneer, Alouette and many others are vehicles that seek out information on the space environment proper. They measure conditions in space: temperatures, pressures, light intensities, different types and levels of radiation, and other factors. These are scientific explorers and automatic laboratories that radio back their messages of conditions in space.

Other satellites rocket into space to develop equipment, procedures and engineering systems, and to achieve a level of reliability to meet future needs. The Air Force Discoverer satellite series is perhaps the best example of the research, engineering and development satellite. Its primary purpose is to seek out information on conditions in space. Engineers also use Discoverers to test stabilization systems. Can a satellite be kept in orbit so that one end of the satellite always points at the earth? Certain experiments require this capability. It is difficult to come by, and shot after shot is needed to attain this goal. This isn't research, it is development engineering.

The Discoverer satellites have turned in a remarkable performance. They go into orbit with astounding regularity and reliability. They have developed the stabilization system we require so badly for virtually every future satellite effort, scientific and military. The Discoverer is about 25 feet long and 5 feet in diameter, big enough to carry out a variety of experiments. It tests communications equipment. It carries slabs of metal which robot arms smack together in space, and then slowly pull apart again. Metal has strange properties in space. One piece tends to stick to another. How hard does it stick? What force is required to separate the metal sheets? Does radiation in space affect the metal and its characteristics? How much outgassing (the loss of molecular particles into vacuum) is involved, and how does this affect the performance of systems under space conditions?

This is the purpose of satellites like Discoverer. We are pouring billions of dollars into military satellite ventures such as Samos, Midas and Saint. We can't send these vehicles into orbit as operational systems without exhaustive and extensive in-orbit research as a preliminary. Discoverer carries this responsibility.

Because the Discoverer is so large, its capacity to carry and contain its engineering development and test systems often goes unfilled for a particular shot. Or, it would go unfilled except that many scientific experiments go along as piggyback riders. Into the available space of the Discoverer satellites go brilliant blinking lights to aid in the development program for Transit navigational satellites and ANNA geodetic survey satellites. Into Discoverer's recoverable capsules go plant and animal spores, biomedical experiments, and other tests where the *recovery* of this material is important to the scientist. Discoverer is the workhorse of the space age.

The third category of satellite is called the practical applications and development vehicle. Transit is a Navy program to develop an all-weather, reliable system of navigational reference points in space that may be used by airplanes or ships. As such, it is sent into space not to ferret out information on conditions that exist in space, but to serve a functional purpose.

Other satellites in this category include the Echo and Telstar vehicles to develop communications systems, and the Tiros series which monitor, and report upon, cloud and weather conditions anywhere on this planet.

The fourth satellite category involves the study of the planet earth itself—not the environment in space, but this world physically. ANNA (which stands for Army, Navy, NASA and Air Force) is a national effort that may provide us with the first truly accurate representations of where our islands and continents really are in relation to one another. It is a geodetic survey vehicle which takes advantage of its altitude above the earth's surface as a reference point.

Other satellites in this category of earth study include vehicles that measure the density of the land masses over which they orbit. The perturbations in the orbital path of the satellites allow scientists to measure accurately the intensity of gravitational pull at different points around the planet. Thus, we are going into space to study the interior of the earth.

The fifth satellite category involves military applications vehicles. These include the Midas satellite system (Missile Defense Alarm System) that studies the earth by infrared surveying technique, and detects the movement of any vehicle at great heat such as a ballistic missile moving up from the atmosphere. This news can be flashed to the U.S. mainland's warning centers and provides almost immediate indication of a ballistic missile (or missiles), or even a spacebound rocket, leaving the area of the USSR.

Samos has the role of conducting extensive photographic reconnaissance of the earth, specifically, of areas within the USSR. Saint is a study system for approaching unknown satellites, studying them, determining if their purpose and mission are hostile, and, if necessary, destroying them.

The sixth category on the satellite list extends the term *satellite* somewhat, since it includes the investigation of other bodies in the solar system. These are the lunar and planetary mission vehicles and the deep space probes—Pioneer, Ranger, Mariner, Surveyor, and others.

The seventh involves the long-range development of aerospace vehicles and systems development, which might be considered as part-and-parcel of the programs for manned space flight. In this area we find Project Mercury, soon to be succeeded by our first two-man spaceship, Gemini. Beyond that lies Apollo, the program to send three astronauts to the vicinity of the moon.

Simultaneously, however, there are other extensive programs

under way. The aerospace vehicle, a machine equally at home in space and within the atmosphere, is the ultimate goal of current technology. The X-15 is a rocket-powered airplane that can streak briefly into the lower edges of space. The X-20 Dyna-Soar is a winged craft that will orbit the earth, re-enter in a long, slow drop back to the atmosphere, and then be flown to a landing by its pilot in the manner of a conventional aircraft.

Another element of the manned space program includes the development of future manned space stations: huge orbiting installations that will circle the earth at a height of several hundred miles, and that will be staffed with regular crews that will remain for weeks and perhaps months in space.

Beyond these initial studies, but an integral element of the programs, are the vehicles that will enable exploitation of the first lunar landings. As these are developed, the systems to send manned expeditions to Mars and Venus will evolve from their progress. The essential part of this effort is that they are all linked as a single, many-faceted entity.

Concurrent efforts, costing many times more than the final vehicles themselves, are the different programs to develop the propulsion systems and booster vehicles to get these robot and manned packages into orbit and on their way to other worlds. Thus there is spun a kaleidoscopic fabric that in its entirety represents the national space effort.

The empty space around the earth seethes with energy. Because of our ability to send observatories and electronic listening stations into orbit, we have been able to scrutinize and to measure vast floods of energy that never pierce the atmospheric mantle and reach our ground instruments. Much of what we have learned has startled scientists.

We have measured ultraviolet and X-rays, radio and infrared radiations, sunspots, solar flares, solar storms; we have studied electromagnetic radiations from the sun and clouds of energetic particles expelled with unbelievable force and magnitude from the sun toward the earth. We have read instruments telling us of great tides and seas of energy; we have learned of sheets of magnetic force. We have watched in awe the interplay of many forces of which we were not even aware before we were able to send instruments away from our planet.

We have learned, for example, that the space some 93,000,000 miles from the sun consists not of emptiness, but of an average of seventy particles per cubic inch. Compared to our former concepts of nothingness, seventy particles per cubic inch seems to make space a very busy thoroughfare. But if we translate this density into familiar terms, we find that 200,000 cubic miles of the interplanetary medium are required simply to equal the material in one cubic inch of our atmosphere at sea level.

To which the man-in-the-street justifiably retorts: "So what does this mean to me?"

And strange to say, it means—in a roundabout fashion—a great deal. First, despite the seeming emptiness of space, it is actually filled with material. If we could add up all the matter floating freely in the vacuum between the stars of our galaxy, we would find that in this vacuum there is enough matter to equal the amount contained in all the stars.

This seems impossible. Consider the massiveness and density of the earth. Then add the moon, and the other planets, of which Jupiter alone has a diameter ten times greater than that of our own world. Add the sun, nearly a million miles in diameter. And then consider the millions of suns, many of them so huge that our sun is trifling in comparison. Millions, and tens of millions, of stars. Unknown millions of planets; perhaps hundreds of millions of planetary bodies.

And "empty space" in this galaxy alone equals all this. The paradox lies in the fact that despite the number of stars and other bodies, the galaxy is almost empty. The explanation is that this amount of matter is spread throughout such an incredibly vast distance that space only seems empty. The distances between the celestial bodies are incomprehensible to us. If we could travel at a speed of more than 670,000,000 miles per hour it would take us more than four years just to reach the star closest to our own.

The discovery of these characteristics of space is important. We can't duplicate such characteristics and environmental conditions in a laboratory. Much more important is the fact that this material is spread through the solar system. It lies between us and the sun.

We've learned that magnetic fields pulsate through the solar system. Fierce electrical storms rage in space. Great electrical winds blow about and across the planets. It is this region, the ninety million miles separating the earth and the sun, that determines much of the weather on this world. The sun pours forth not only its familiar light and heat, but also vast and terrible barrages of energy. These are affected by gravitational tides, by magnetic belts and zones, by great spheres and patterns of radiation. These forces create the earth's ionosphere and paint the auroras in the night skies. They tear great gaps in the ionosphere, the electrical atmosphere hundreds of miles above the earth, and thus impair radio communication.

For it is the ionosphere which reflects radio waves transmitted from the surface of the earth and bounces them back to receiving stations. When we discuss the properties of the ionosphere in the scientific sense, we're talking beyond the sphere of everyday life. But when the radio receives squealing static, that static comes not from deficiencies in the set, but perhaps from a great storming cloud of electrical particles released from the sun hours or days before that is now blanketing the earth and raising electrical hell within the ionosphere.

Suddenly regular communications disappear into fits of radio silence. Static drowns out reception. Some stations can't receive anything. To the individual at home, it is annoying and bothersome, but it is not a life-or-death matter.

It is of extreme urgency to other people. Scientific outposts in Antarctica and other outlying areas have been completely cut off from the world by storms originating on the sun's surface. Ships on the more distant trade lanes of the world might be in serious difficulties during a time of solar activity. Their radioed pleas for help go unanswered because the great rifts in the ionosphere swallow up their messages and spit them out into space, instead of reflecting them back to earth.

Airplanes suddenly find they cannot communicate with either land stations or ships. Their navigational aids begin to go haywire. Magnetic storms shriek silently beyond and within the atmosphere, and compasses spin or jerk erratically.

No longer does the study of electrical layers two hundred miles high fall within the category of "pure scientific research." Understanding the nature of the solar-spawned storms and their effect on the electrical atmosphere can mean a difference of survival or death to many people who, in an emergency, must have reliable communications.

Then there is the effect on our military defenses. There are nuclear submarines at sea which must communicate by radio. Hundreds of great bombers in the air, picket aircraft flying radar patrol, warships at sea, fighters on intercept duty—the list goes on and on. An ionospheric storm, especially in the northern polar regions, absolutely disrupts our ability to maintain tight communications and control throughout our far-flung military forces. In times of alert or emergency, military units cut off from Washington because of communications disruption may be useless.

Such disturbances in the polar regions led directly to the launching aboard a Thor-Agena B of the first Canadian satellite, the Alouette I.

Alouette I was designed, prepared, built and tested in its entirety by Canadian scientists. Coordination between the two countries went through the offices of the National Aeronautics and Space Administration (NASA). NASA in turn worked directly with the Air Force and the Department of Defense. The Air Force supplied to NASA a Thor-Agena B vehicle from its Discoverer program. The launch was carried out by Air Force operational crews from Vandenberg Air Force Base in California. The satellite went into a polar orbit, i.e., north to south, as the first such scientific firing by the United States (although it was preceded by several dozen military shots—Air Force Discoverer, Midas, and Samos satellites—in this orbital plane).

Conditions in the polar regions don't apply to the rest of the world. An unusual feature of the polar and subpolar ionosphere results from the continuous daylight in summer and continuous night during the winter. This causes seasonal variations in the polar atmosphere's illumination. A further complication in the ionosphere at high latitudes is caused by the effects on ionization of charged particles from the sun.

Scientists consider the main characteristics of the auroral ionosphere to be diversity, variability and abnormality. The auroral ionosphere is a great big scientific headache. It is a fountainhead of disturbances. On its rare quiet occasions it settles down and behaves with normal characteristics by nicely reflecting radio waves. But only rarely.

From the standpoint of communications needs, the worst ionospheric condition is the "polar blackout." During these times reflection disappears almost completely. Special research instruments used to count electron density (ionograms, or plots of electrons versus altitude) show completely blank sheets. During such periods radio communications disappear completely.

The polar blackout is similar to the "sudden ionosphere disturbances" which throughout the hemisphere produce abrupt and simultaneous radio fadeout, lasting from ten to sixty minutes. The polar blackout doesn't come with the abrupt speed of the hemispheric disturbances, but it may last continuously during daylight hours for as long as a week.

Then there is the "ionospheric storm," which becomes greatly intensified in the auroral zones. The ionosphere loses its placidity and becomes stirred with great heaving movements and tearing of the electrical atmosphere fabric. The number of frequencies which may be used for communications is reduced greatly, and even the frequencies which can be used fluctuate rapidly and unexpectedly in signal intensity. Scientists have learned that the "ionospheric storm" is usually accompanied by a magnetic storm, or by a period of severe and unusual fluctuation in terrestrial magnetic intensity.

The only method of obtaining certain vital studies of electron-density profiles is to send satellites into orbit above the ionosphere, and then take measurements from this "topside" vantage. "In addition to its scientific value," explains a NASA scientist, "the increased knowledge of the ionosphere is directly applicable to communications and tracking applications."

Scientists have found it necessary to conduct a series of major research and study efforts on space, rather than to concentrate on only one area such as the ionospheric studies carried out by Alouette I. Other satellites penetrate different areas and conduct their scrutiny of the electrical atmosphere and other space radiation conditions along as great a part of the spectrum as our instruments will allow.

But if one particular picture were to be drawn from the more than five years of research with these scientific satellites, it might properly be described as being a growing and amazing view of the vast interplay of forces in space. Not too many decades ago we suffered from near blindness in our picture of the atom. It was the smallest item in nature. It could not be divided. Now the atom is a huge and empty place, compared to the indivisible unit we once thought it was. If we could take a uranium atom and expand it until the outer shell of orbiting electrons was as huge as Madison Square Garden, we would see only the thinnest fog at the very edges of the Garden and a single shining marble in the center. The rest is empty space.

Similarly, the profusion of forces and particles in space is staggering. Some scientists believe that space is occupied (in the inter-planetary medium) by about 70 particles per cubic inch. Other scientists place the figure higher, 100 particles per cubic inch, plus a lesser number of energetic cosmic rays.

The charting of the interplanetary medium is fantastic. Scientists are laboriously creating their "building blocks" of space. They con-clude that normally there is less than one energetic cosmic ray per cubic yard. We must remember that such rays move at almost the velocity of light (186,271 miles per second) and that such occu-pation of a cubic yard of space is very transitory indeed. There is also a small interplanetary magnetic field of "about two gamma in magnitude, which is to say about one ten-thousandth the strength of the earth's magnetic field at the equator."

Scientists are charting the streams and tidal forces of space. The huge flares crashing outward from the sun have greater mean-ing today than they did before the era of satellites. When such a solar flare occurs, an enormous tongue of relatively slow moving charged particles (plasma) erupts from the solar surface at the source of the flare. This plasma tongue lunges through space at about one thousand miles per second—which is slow movement in space, but barely comprehensible to us. This is two hundred times faster than the speed of a satellite orbiting the earth.

Moving through space at this speed, the plasma cloud reaches our planet about twenty-six hours after leaving the sun. Its passage creates great violence in the space medium. As it moves inexorably earthward it drags with it lines of solar magnetic force. These are frozen into the cloud, forced by electromagnetic laws to move with it. The lines of magnetic force have their roots on the surface of the sun, but as the plasma cloud sails toward the earth, the magnetic force lines become tremendously extended, like a one-inch rubber band stretched out to the length of a city block or more.

Finally the plasma cloud sweeps over and completely envelops the area of space, including the earth. The Van Allen radiation belts heave and writhe in response to the forces suddenly imposed upon them. Magnetic storms rage; auroral displays appear in their wavering, brilliant, shifting patterns in the northern heavens. But the plasma tongue has a delayed effect. The solar magnetic field lines maintain a funneling channel to the sun. Any subsequent flares with their erupting plasma tongues will send these great force clouds speeding along the channel at greater speed and intensity to the earth.

As the study of the spatial forces continued, other facts began to emerge—and some of them were alarming to scientists. There was the "population of low-energy protons" within the inner Van Allen radiation belt. Extensive studies made it clear that the low-energy protons (subatomic particles) increase enormously in number at certain altitudes and latitudes when great activity takes place on the surface of the sun. The protons stream with vast energy into the upper regions of the earth's electrical atmosphere in the polar regions. As the protons storm lower toward the earth, they generate neutrons in the atmosphere. The neutrons, as they decay in energy, in turn produce more protons—which then become trapped in the radiation belt about the earth.

Scientists examined their available data, and then sent additional satellites into orbits that swung far from the earth, cutting through the different zones of the radiation belt. During November 1960, the sun erupted with great electrical storms. These caused wild fluctuations in the earth's electrical atmosphere and radiation belts.

Had a man been orbiting the earth in the vicinity of the Van Allen radiation belts during the great solar flares of November 1960, he would have returned to earth a dying man. The total radiation dose caused by solar protons at the time exceeded 700 roentgens; a 400 roentgen exposure is considered fatal to half the people exposed.

So the observation of solar flares became indispensable in terms of carrying out space flight programs. It is necessary to study the sun so meticulously that we can predict the time and nature and severity of the solar eruptions. If we are aware that a solar flare is to occur during a week when a manned space flight is planned, that flight must be delayed. The Soviets perform spectacular work in this field, and none of their manned space flights have taken place without careful study of solar conditions.

With our increasing knowledge, we are predicting future times of great solar disturbances and modifying development programs of our manned space effort. Evidence to date indicates that the relative effect of the sun upon the earth changes by critical factors over the eleven-year "solar cycle." During this period sunspot activity goes from a minimum to a maximum and then back to a minimum.

Scientists consider the solar flares, which to date seem to occur sporadically and unpredictably, as the hurricanes or typhoons of space flight. Top space scientists say that these solar flares "need to be studied in detail on an urgent basis so that the information can be used to assure that manned spacecraft, such as Apollo, will have a maximum chance for either avoiding the storms or of being designed to protect the astronauts from the effects of the storm."

If it were possible to gather all the electrons from the artificial radiation belt created by the nuclear explosion in space of July 9, 1962, we might be somewhat disappointed when we looked at the results. The total mass of all the electrons in the vast belts curving about the earth would come to less than one-tenth of an ounce. Yet so high are the energies of such particles and so great is their effect that they have demanded intensive scientific study, affecting as they do activities in the electrical zones and envelopes about earth.

Another satellite investigation program, as a separate example of our scientific studies of space, is the S-3a, an 89-pound vehicle designed to determine the population of high-energy particles in space as well as their energies. The S-3a area of responsibility covers the magnetosphere and the regions of interplanetary space beyond. The magnetosphere begins several hundred miles up and then extends to several thousand miles out into space. We don't know why it extends to this distance, but we do know that it was in this region that we discovered the Van Allen radiation belts.

One of the most vital points of understanding in the years of accumulated space research we have conducted is that our work has opened door after door. Every time a satellite sent back data, our knowledge broadened enormously. And every time we widened our horizons, we were plagued with still more unanswered scientific questions.

The first satellite launched by this country—Explorer I on January 31, 1958—established the existence of energetic particles trapped above the earth. We also learned that the terrestrial magnetic field functioned as a sort of enormous storage bin for the particles of matter that spiraled around the earth's magnetic force lines. (A cross-section view would show the storage bin in the shape of a lima bean.)

But that was about the limit of what the first small satellite taught us. Other vehicles stripped away other mysteries by answering such questions as how many particular particles of a certain energy range could be found at a particular time under certain conditions in a particular area of space. Despite the years of these satellite successes, we cannot today produce an accurate model of the vast and tremendous interplay of forces just beyond this world. It will require many more satellites and the successive accumulation of knowledge to probe still deeper toward the truth.

The early satellite flights led our scientists to conclude definitely that the Van Allen radiation consisted of two distinct belts, one of electrons and the other of protons. Only a succession of satellites and an accumulation of data disproved the new theory, and established that in fact no such distinction existed. Instead, we now look upon the magnetosphere as one huge trapping region in which particles with different characteristics are caught in various areas of space.

Even magnetic field measurements in space have led us a merry scientific chase. Vanguard III provided one of the first measurements from space of our planetary magnetic field. Then, Pioneer V and Explorer X began to measure the area in space where the earth's magnetic field tapered off to a leveling factor, and the interplanetary magnetic field became dominant. Then another satellite again disturbed this picture. Explorer XII pinpointed the precise area, but added the news that there is probably a turbulent transition region between the terrestrial and the interplanetary magnetic fields.

The plastic *mylar* can be formed to a thickness of only 0.0005 of an inch. And it can be coated with aluminum vapor with unbelievable precision to an additional millionth of an inch. Finished, it is a plastic for space duty that is only half the thickness of the cellophane on a package of cigarettes. Remember an unusual property of mylar—it has a tensile strength one third that of steel.

Take this material, fold it again and again until it fits into a container only 26 inches in diameter. Clamp the container to the top of a rocket, and hurl the whole thing into space until it goes into orbit a thousand miles above the earth. Now, eject the folded plastic into the space vacuum. Then ignite thirty pounds of sublimating powder, a powder which doesn't burn, but flashes directly from a powder into a gas.

Some minutes later you have a brilliant spherical satellite one hundred feet in diameter and as tall as a ten-story building.

Echo is well-known to Americans as the first passive communications satellite. Engineers bounced radio and television messages off the shiny reflecting surface of Echo in a series of communications experiments, to determine whether or not passive satellite relays would be effective for global communications.

But this turned out to be only one aspect of Echo, the ghostly satellite that paid unexpected dividends in re-emphasizing that space may be a vacuum, but that it is also filled with floods of radiations and strange winds of great force.

On August 12, 1962, the Echo satellite completed its second year of orbiting the earth. The once shiny, spherical shape had lost its beauty. Although still bright because of the vaporized aluminum on its surface, Echo was wrinkled and prune-like in its appearance. For two years uncounted thousands of tiny dust particles moving at 25,000 miles per hour had penetrated Echo's skin.

But Echo had some surprises. In her first two years of orbiting life (she's still up and may be for many years to come), the spherical bag orbited the planet 9,000 times—a total distance of 277,257,677.67 miles.

Echo proved, to the delight of engineers, that an inflatable structure in space can survive for a long time. The condition of the satellite, deteriorating slowly, provided the clues by which engineers could design better, more durable materials for advanced inflatable structures of the future. Echo II will be 135 feet in diameter and semi-rigid, strengthened from within to maintain its spherical shape even though the gas may escape.

To scientists the most unexpected results from Echo came from its great size and little mass. As we learned more about the forces sweeping through space, it became evident that Echo was unusually sensitive to both solar radiation and drag from the tenuous particles a thousand miles high.

Whenever a storm erupts on the surface of the sun and the great clouds of energetic particles stream earthward, scientists pay close attention to the orbital movement of Echo. She responds visibly to the force of the solar winds. Her orbit varies from a circle to an ellipse, depending upon the intensity of the winds.

When first launched, Echo sailed in an orbit with an apogee (point farthest from the earth) of 1,049 miles and a perigee (point nearest the earth) of 945 miles, an excellent circular orbit. Approximately eighteen months later the apogee increased to 1,350

miles and the perigee decreased to only 580 miles. Then, the sun
spat forth its violence, and the space winds blew harshly. The orbit
shrank to an apogee of 1,175 miles and the perigee extended upward to 704 miles.

Quick as we were to seize the knowledge of our first satellites,
we were equally quick to draw final conclusions from what we
learned in our initial efforts. And then, somewhat more slowly, we
learned that our early acquisitions of knowledge did not in fact
strip the veils of mystery from the space environment, but allowed
us only to peer into the wonders of the universe.

An old saying of Dr. Albert Einstein's on mathematics seemed
perfectly adapted to the problems of the space scientists: "Insofar
as mathematics applies to reality it is not certain and so far as
mathematics is certain it does not apply to reality."

This has come to be the dilemma of the scientists investigating
the wonders of the universe—and of the earth and its immediate
environs. Much of what scientists have accumulated will require
many months and even years for analysis and extrapolation.

The early and succeeding Explorer series satellites furnished us
information on radiation zones, micrometeoroids, temperatures in
space, radiation and magnetic storms, ion and electron composition of the ionosphere, behavior of energetic particles, gamma
rays streaming earthward from the sun and celestial sources, and
other characteristics of space. The three Vanguard satellites added
substantially to this knowledge. And then came the more special-
ized research satellites. As part of this series there are the international ionosphere satellites—part of the series in the US International Program of space research—such as the British Ariel and
the Canadian Alouette.

The days of the old satellite are not only numbered, they are
already relegated to history. One of the problems with our basic
research space program involved the design of the satellites. They

had to conform to the limited weight and size of existing booster rockets. Those shapes and weights were not the best for research, but they simply had to do.

A new era is upon us. The time of custom-built satellites is gone, and in its place basic research is being carried out in a methodical manner. We have now accepted a philosophy for future space research employing a series of standardized satellites—including the orbiting solar, astronomical and geophysical observatories.

The standardized satellite is a basic structure, complete with its power supply, telemetry, data storage facilities and other equipment fundamental to its research mission. It is built on the principle of modular compartments, so that it may carry out many experiments during a single orbiting mission. The new approach will undoubtedly result in great savings of both time and cost, as well as assuring much greater efficiency. Each of the standardized satellite's modules will be a simple, electronic building block that may be plugged into the satellite. Thus, the over-all structure, the shell and its housings, may be fabricated independently and at much lower cost than before.

One of the new satellite series, the Orbiting Astronomical Observatory (OAO) will be able to observe the solar system and the universe with large telescopes from a vantage point beyond the atmosphere. To the astronomer the atmosphere is a muddy and turbulent sea, and the OAO is about to realize a long-held dream of observations beyond this murky zone. To astronomers, the 3,200-pound OAO satellite series promises unprecedented knowledge of the planets, the stars and the composition of space itself.

Orbiting about 500 miles above the earth, the OAO satellites will each contain about 1,000 pounds of experimental equipment such as telescopes, spectrometers and photometers. The remainder of the payload will contain the elaborate stabilization system, power supplies and telemetry system for transmitting data back to earth. Each OAO will have two silicon solar-cell paddles and nickel-cadmium batteries, to furnish a minimum usable power supply of 270 watts. The satellites will be huge by present Explorer standards; each OAO will be nearly 10 feet high, 6.6 feet in width and 16.2 feet wide with its solar paddles extended.

The Orbiting Solar Observatory (OSO) series will conduct extensive studies of the sun and of solar phenomena from a point well beyond the levels of the atmosphere where disruptive effects might interfere with observations. Different missions will carry different equipment, but essentially the OSO vehicles will go into orbit with instruments such as X-ray and Lyman Alpha spectrometers, neutron flux sensors and gamma ray monitors. The early OSO satellites will be more than 3 feet high, 44 inches in diameter, and will weigh about 350 pounds each. As larger boosters become available, the size of the OSO observatories will increase.

Third in the new standardized series of satellites will be the Orbiting Geophysical Observatory (OGO). Each of these new vehicles will be able to conduct fifty separate geophysical experiments during a single orbital mission. The scientific mission for each of the OGO flights is expected to vary considerably, but the same satellite structure will prevail.

Unlike the other vehicles in the new satellite series, the OGO satellites will be launched on the basis of a regular schedule into carefully preassigned trajectories. For each of these trajectories, the basic OGO designation will be modified or extended. When rocketed into a high eccentric orbit with a perigee of 150 miles and an apogee of some 60,000 miles, the name OGO will be replaced by the designation EGO (Eccentric Geophysical Observatory). In this role, EGO will be assigned missions to study energetic particles, magnetic fields and other geophysical phenomena which can properly be evaluated only by such an eccentric orbit.

Some of the OGO satellites will launch from Canaveral, others will boost from Vandenberg in California into polar orbits. For these missions OGO becomes POGO (Polar Orbiting Geophysical Observatory), and the orbits will extend from 140 miles perigee to 500 miles apogee. The POGO satellites will carry out research begun with Alouette, and will concentrate upon atmospheric and ionospheric studies, particularly in the polar regions.

OGO satellite vehicles will be some six feet long and three feet across, excluding the solar paddles, and will each weigh about 900 pounds (including 150 pounds of instruments). Depending upon the availability of larger booster vehicles, later versions of OGO will increase in weight to 1,500 pounds, and include a spherical satellite carried piggyback. Once in orbit, the spherical satellite will be ejected to conduct associated observations.

OGO will resemble a spindly satellite creature for many of its missions. Experimental sensors will be placed on booms which will extend well outward from the main OGO body. This will be done to prevent the satellite bulk from interfering with certain observations and experiments.

The pattern for basic research in space is thus clearly established. In the initial phases of our national program of space exploration we used anything available as a booster. This procedure could not be avoided. The problem was to get into space, and get there quickly.

Our first year of satellite firings involved a failure rate higher than fifty percent. The actual loss of experimentation was considerably greater, since not all the satellites that did go into orbit functioned as planned, or for as long as had been expected. Now the standardized vehicle satellite provides great hopes for overcoming these deficiencies. However, where the smaller payloads are involved, we have little problem in continuing our basic studies of space.

The Thor-Delta, for example, failed in its first mission and then turned in the tremendous performance of fifteen consecutive successes. Thor-Delta is a relatively low-powered booster vehicle. It fails to meet requirements for heavy payloads. Even the powerful Atlas-Agena, which can boost 5,000 pounds into a low orbit, will not meet many of our needs.

The key to continued programs on a steady and efficient basis is propulsion. Right now the booster program of the United States is in serious difficulty. The failure of the Centaur program, with the designed capability of sending a payload of 8,500 pounds into a 300-mile orbit, or of firing an 1,800-pound payload to the moon, has been especially crippling. The NASA schedule called for eleven Centaur firings in 1963 alone, and more than one hundred Centaur missions through the remainder of the decade.

But Centaur will not be operational until 1965 at the earliest. What effect this will have on future programs is impossible to determine at this time, but several programs have already been canceled, others stretched out in development time, and still others reduced greatly in weight to fit smaller and less powerful boosters.

A grain of salt is necessary in any extrapolation of future time-tables. Not all of the satellites launched will go into orbit. Not all of the satellites orbited will function as planned. Lists of future accomplishments must always be suspect.

In 1961 NASA launched seven scientific satellites and only three succeeded. In the same year NASA launched six deep space probes, and by stretching a point can claim success for two. This is not a particularly good batting average, and certainly it resulted in much less data than our scientists had hoped for.

The Congressional hearings for the 1963 NASA budget provide dramatic proof of how the best-laid plans go awry. NASA planned for two Ranger deep space probes in 1961. Both were launched; both failed. In 1962 three Rangers were on the schedule. Again all three were launched and all three failed. Obviously, the plans for acquiring data on the moon and the lunar space environment have come to an alarming halt.

For 1963, NASA has already canceled Ranger VI, but still hopes to schedule three Ranger missions with Atlas-Agena B booster rockets. What percentage of success or of failure can we expect? Despite different missions in which different levels of success were attained in the past, all five of the Ranger missions have failed in their primary assignments. When the boosters failed, the spacecraft worked perfectly. When the boosters worked perfectly, the spacecraft failed.

For 1964, NASA planned four Surveyor missions with the Centaur vehicle. This can be erased from any future list. As for the five Surveyor missions with Centaur boosters planned for 1965, there is little indication that the boosters will be available.

There are hidden, nagging problems. Centaur originally was to send a Surveyor payload of 2,500 pounds to the moon. The Surveyor is an elaborate lunar study vehicle in two versions. One is to orbit the moon for extended in-space research; the other is to land on the moon and carry out robot research activities. But even before the Centaur program failed on its availability schedules, it suffered a serious cutback in payload capability. The extensive plans for the 2,500-pound probe had to be reduced to only 2,100 pounds. Then additional difficulties were encountered, and the scientists saw another reduction to 1,800 pounds. They stated flatly that reducing the payload to this figure would jeopardize the mission so seriously it might not be carried out at all.

NASA also planned a mission in 1965 for its Prospector vehicle, a massive payload to be soft-landed on the moon. The Prospector is able to rove about the lunar surface under automatic control and to carry out a mobile study of lunar conditions. Three such missions are planned for 1965—these with the Saturn C-1 booster. But the huge Saturn itself is behind schedule, the 1965 date looks somewhat doubtful, and the entire Prospector program may now be abandoned.

We planned a series of interplanetary studies to Venus and to Mars. The 1962 schedule called for two Mariner shots to Venus with the Centaur vehicle. Obviously, these were never made. Instead, we pushed the Atlas-Agena into the breach by cutting down drastically on the payload. The first booster had to be destroyed in flight when it drifted off course. The second Mariner shot proved to be a brilliant success, but one tempered by the forced reduction in payload.

No Atlas-Agena B Mariner probes are planned for 1963. One is scheduled for Centaur. That mission may be canceled; perhaps it will be replaced with the Atlas-Agena B, but this is by no means certain. For 1964 there are six missions scheduled to the planets, two with Atlas-Agena B and four with Centaur. Scratch the four for Centaur.

On a long-range basis of experiments that require powerful boosters, we are in a mess. Perhaps we will be able to extricate ourselves from our plight, but at the moment, the most enthusiastic scheduling for the future is riddled with doubts and uncertainties. Certainly we will make extensive deep space and other probes, and just as certainly many of those research missions will be conducted with payloads reduced drastically in size, weight and capability because of the lack of powerful boosters.

What does seem much closer to realization in the immediate future is the new standardized-satellite series. The present NASA schedule calls for the launching of three Explorers in 1963, five in 1964, and nine in 1965. The OGO schedule lists two shots in 1963, and four each in 1964 and 1965. The OSO schedule calls for two shots in 1963, three in 1964, and four in 1965.

Somewhat less promising is the OAO. The ultimate guiding accuracy of this system is expected to approach 0.1 second of arc. "This is about equivalent," explains a NASA scientist, "to the accuracy required to use a telescope located in Baltimore to pick out either the right or left eye of an individual in Washington for detailed study as to its color and brightness."

Obviously, the development of the OAO system demands extraordinary engineering effort. The NASA schedule calls for orbiting two OAO vehicles in 1964, and another two in 1965. The schedule is now seriously threatened. NASA is suffering from acute financial shortages, and the boosters to send the 3,200-pound satellite into orbits about 475 miles high may not be available in this time.

The basic research vehicles of our space program include those ferreting out the secrets of space in terms of radiation, pressure, temperature, interplanetary matter density, study of the sun, and research in similar areas. These satellite vehicles and their programs, however, do not include many other packages sent whirling into orbit about the earth—the applications satellites.

The latter are meteorological, communications, navigation and geodetic survey vehicles. They are distinct from the basic research satellite programs in that their purpose is to supply a service. They are a direct return for the money, whereas the basic research vehicles are assigned essentially to a study of conditions.

The original Echo program is now considered as accomplished, although Echo I still serves in its unexpected capacity of swaying to the solar winds, gravitational tides and other forces in space. But NASA has great hopes for its new Echo series. First, a single Echo II will be orbited for additional tests. Its greater rigidity means that it will serve as an effective communications relay for a longer period of time than did Echo I. And the new Echo II satellite is but the basic test vehicle for Project Rebound.

In this new system, a single major launch vehicle will carry three 600-pound Echo II satellites into a circular orbit 1,500 miles high. There, the three satellites will go into a free-drifting cluster. The multiple sphere system permits great savings in money and equipment, and assures that the satellites will be orbited simultaneously for extensive communications experimentation. If the passive system works out as planned, NASA may launch enough vehicles so that forty to fifty of the giant Echo II balloons will simultaneously be orbiting the earth.

Hard-headed engineers scoff at this NASA plan. They insist that the giant passive communications satellite is a clumsy means of achieving space communications. They predict—despite the NASA

studies and proposals—that Rebound will end up on the scrap
heap. And with the budget shortages already crimping NASA
where it hurts the most, there is now every chance that Rebound
will never extend beyond its lofty paper plans.

Easily the best known of all unmanned satellites today is Telstar
—the first experimental active-repeater communications satellite
that ushered in the era of live television transmissions on a transcontinental basis. The 34-inch, 150-pound Telstar satellites are
not the ultimate design in communications space vehicles. They
represent an experimental system that will establish more clearly
than at present the possibilities and restrictions of the active-
repeater system.

A television transmission is beamed from the sending station on
earth to Telstar in space. Telstar picks up the signal, amplifies it
and beams the signal back to earth.

Telstar deserves added notice in that it represents the first commercial space vehicle ever placed in orbit. NASA entered into contract with American Telephone and Telegraph. AT&T designed,
built, tested and delivered the satellite to NASA and also con-
structed elaborate transmission and receiving ground facilities.
NASA, in turn, provided the launching vehicle, launched the rocket
into orbit, carried out all necessary tracking and global-wide data
receiving, for which AT&T paid the entire bill, at absolutely no
cost to the space program.

Two Telstars were scheduled for orbital tests; the second will
soon be launched. The first Telstar proved highly effective and productive of research information. But AT&T scientists feel there is
still more data to be gained with a second launching of the experimental satellite vehicle.

Other communications satellites programs have been rushed
into their first orbits. Perhaps the best publicized of these was
the new Project Relay vehicle. This is a NASA program for developing the technology for a communications satellite system of
the active-repeater type, but based upon engineering principles

somewhat different from those of Telstar. The Relay satellites will act, in effect, as tiny microwave towers in the heavens, looping the earth in elliptical orbits extending from 1,000 to 3,000 miles (and later, to 6,000 miles). Relay involves a global cooperative effort, in that several countries around the world will work closely with the United States. In its ultimate form, as many as a dozen or more of the 125-pound Relays will simultaneously orbit the planet in order to provide constant coverage. The satellites will be spaced carefully, so that one or more satellites will always be high above the earth between continents and in position to transmit live television and radio broadcasts.

Beyond Relay lies Syncom, the satellite system for which there is the greatest communications hope. Syncom is an advanced experiment which combines the features of the active-repeater satellite with a unique orbit. The latter is a synchronous orbit which will place the Syncom satellites into orbit at a height of 22,300 miles. The orbits must be above the equator and lie in the equatorial plane, so that each satellite swings around the world at the same speed at which the surface of the earth rotates beneath it. By matching these two speeds, the Syncom will orbit the earth in the same time that the earth rotates on its axis. The satellite will remain relatively stationary over one point on the earth. The final plan is to have three or four Syncom satellites in orbit, equidistant from each other. Thus, at any time, the satellites will be in a position to conduct communications transmissions to virtually any point on the globe.

In the initial test NASA did not try for the equatorial orbit. Instead, the 55-pound Syncom satellite was to orbit the earth in a path inclined about thirty degrees to the equator (similar to that of the Mercury spacecraft). Because of its 22,300-mile height, Syncom in the early tests will travel north and south across the equator, but will remain more or less fixed about a given longitude. When the system is proven, NASA will try the equatorial orbit.

The initial Syncom launching was a particularly frustrating experience. The booster rocket sent the satellite into what scientists claim was the desired orbit. Then, mystifyingly, Syncom "disappeared." At this writing no one knows if the transmitters simply went dead, or if the final orbit proved so unusual that we could not with any accuracy locate the satellite.

A parallel program for the synchronous-orbiting satellite system is a military effort known as Advent. As with Syncom, the United States Army hopes to place three of the heavy (500 pounds each in redesigned form) Advent satellites into synchronous orbits above the equator. Unfortunately, this effort has been plagued with difficulties, not the least of which has been the unavailability of the Centaur booster scheduled for this program. At last count, Advent may be scrapped.

As part of the long-range military communications satellite program, the Army sent its Courier I-B vehicle into a high circular orbit on October 4, 1960. This 500-pound satellite performed brilliantly, and its great weight permitted a multiplicity of experiments. Nineteen days after it entered orbit, however, Courier I-B suffered an "undetermined malfunction," and the satellite went dead. Successful orbiting is not always consistent with the ability to conduct a program through the satellite's planned active lifetime, and this must always be kept in mind when one considers "completely successful" satellite ventures.

There is little argument that the most productive and the most promising of all the satellite programs undertaken by the United States has been the Tiros series, the forerunner of satellite systems which will vastly increase and improve observation of meteorological conditions here on earth. Tiros (Television and Infra-Red Observation Satellite) vehicles have already turned in the most spectacular performance of any space projects system, and it is this vehicle that represents our space engineering and scientific capabilities at their best.

Each of the drum-shaped Tiros satellites is about 19 inches high and some 42 inches in diameter. Tiros weighs from 270 to 285 pounds, and presents to the viewer a glittering façade of 9,200 solar cells which convert solar radiation into electricity for equipment operation. The average household lamp requires about 100 watts of power. But Tiros, despite its television cameras and infrared sensors to measure reflected solar radiation and emitted terrestrial heat radiation, performs splendidly on only 20 watts. Miniaturization of equipment, of course, is the answer.

The performance of the Tiros satellites has been so effective they simply do not reflect an experimental program. Since their inception in April 1960, the Tiros satellites have accomplished these broad goals:

1. Demonstrated that the meteorological satellite concept is practical from the engineering standpoint.
2. Provided cloud cover photographs on a "real-time" basis for immediate use in daily weather forecasts, opening a new era in weather forecasting.
3. Identified hurricanes and typhoons, located them with respect to land masses and followed their movement.
4. Distinguished itself as a vehicle for ice study and ice reconnaissance (for floes and bergs).
5. Provided data leading to the eventual development of an automated cloud pattern identification system, based on the shape and brightness of clouds.
6. Obtained data for the measurement of solar radiation of the earth's atmosphere.

Even the Tiros I satellite turned in a dazzling performance. During its 78 days of operation, the first of the experimental weather satellites transmitted more than 19,000 usable photographs of earth's cloud cover for weather analysis purposes. Above all, Tiros I inaugurated a new era in weather observation by permitting rapid coverage of vast areas of the earth to which meteorologists had previously been blind.

Tiros II (orbited on November 23, 1960) produced more than 23,000 usable photographs, and startled its own engineers by operating for twelve months. Tiros II produced photographs of ice pack conditions in the Gulf of St. Lawrence, and provided invaluable data for predicting weather patterns for the suborbital flight of Alan Shepard in May 1961.

By the time that Tiros III went into orbit (July 12, 1961), meteorologists were turning from experimental data to application of the satellite's observations. All six of the hurricanes that stormed the Caribbean and Atlantic in the 1961 season were identified and tracked by Tiros III; Hurricane Esther was spotted by Tiros two full days before conventional methods located that particular storm. Tiros III provided information which resulted in seventy storm advisories being issued—to the Far East, Latin America, the Indian Ocean, and the continental United States. Tiros III reports were integrated in weather analyses, and were used as the method of weather observation for major space missions. The Navy counted on Tiros III data to schedule its 1961 resupply mission to the Antarctic.

Those were the first three, and Tiros IV, V and VI continued to exceed all hopes in operational capabilities. By the close of 1962 the storm warnings and advisories mounted to many hundreds. The fifth Tiros in the summer of 1962 observed every tropical storm (hurricanes and typhoons) that roared across the oceans. And Tiros V gave first warning of half the world's ten most serious storms in August 1962.

Narrowing results down to a specific area, Tiros III in the summer of 1961 reported a serious buildup of cloud formations in the Gulf of Mexico. The formations rapidly grew into a howling storm, and Hurricane Carla hurtled toward Gulf communities. Officials of the cities and towns blasted by the storm said that the early warning provided by Tiros III saved more money than had been spent in the entire Tiros program, not to mention the lives saved.

NASA hopes to send into orbit early in 1963 its second-generation meteorological satellite, the first Nimbus. A husky vehicle weighing more than six hundred pounds, the first Nimbus satellite of the new series will orbit the earth at a height of 500 miles. Nimbus contains certain features that represent major advances over Tiros.

The satellites will be much larger and heavier. They will contain more elaborate equipment, more powerful energy sources. They will be equipped with horizon scanners and reaction control devices that will keep the television cameras pointed constantly toward the earth. (Tiros lacked this capability.) It could be said that Nimbus eliminates the basic problems of Tiros.

Nimbus satellites will orbit the earth in the polar regions. Launched from Vandenberg, they will gain all the great advantages of polar orbits, and provide the first space pictures of weather patterns of the poles. (Or, at least, the first pictures that will be released, since dozens of Discoverer, Samos, Midas and other Air Force "secret" satellites have orbited the same regions.) An added advantage of the polar orbit is that while Nimbus sweeps around the world from north to south, the planet rotates from west to east beneath the orbital track, and the result will be complete coverage of the entire world.

Beyond Nimbus lies Project Aeros, an advanced meteorological system that may become the first fully operational spaceborne weather observation and forecasting effort. The Aeros satellites would go into orbit at 22,300 miles above the equator—into synchronous orbit. Several Aeros satellites would be put in orbit at equidistant intervals. Since each satellite points its cameras constantly at the earth, the result is complete and constant coverage at all times of the entire surface of the planet.

The Aeros satellites as presently conceived will actually complement the Nimbus system, rather than replace it. Each Aeros satellite would provide its continuous coverage of some twenty-five percent of the entire earth in the tropical and temperate latitudes, while the Nimbus vehicles concentrated upon the polar regions, ice packs, and the "caverns at the top of the world where weather is born," in the words of one meteorologist in the program. One added new feature in Aeros will be a television camera with a variable focus lens such as a Zoomar for closeup views of particular storm areas.

Our accomplishments to date in scientific satellites, in weather vehicles and in many other areas have been impressive, meaningful and formidable. Yet it would be unwise to assume from these accomplishments that we lead the competition in the struggle for technological supremacy in our investigations beyond the earth. There is very little to prove that such supremacy is really ours.

There is much more to the exploration, the exploitation and ultimately the conquest of space than what we have accomplished to date or even what we hope to accomplish. There is another facet of the space scene to be examined, what we have *not* accomplished, what we have *not* done, and, also, where we have failed. Not merely in the operation of our mechanical devices, but in the execution of programs and in our dim foresight of future years and the events that will shape the destinies of both the United States and the USSR.

Not too long ago we were willing to make lofty forecasts not simply of what the future held generally, but specifically of what we would do. We printed timetables, and we exhibited our absolute confidence in the fulfillment of those timetables.

Those sheets of paper are perhaps better forgotten. Better forgotten, too, is the practice of grandiose claims to capture the imagination of the public, claims that very neatly distort facts so that failures become triumphs.

In the late summer of 1962 a NASA lecturer explained the intricacies of space exploration. This man in all seriousness told his audience that "A couple of months ago we placed on the dark side of the moon a lunar probe."

If ever a failure has been cloaked as a success, this is such an incident. The Ranger lunar probe to which the lecturer referred failed miserably in its specified mission of conducting instrument and television studies of the moon, and of landing a seismometer in operating condition on the lunar surface.

Instead, its power sources cold and lifeless, its reaction jets and stabilization systems dead, its main transmitter mute, the Ranger tumbled end over end and gyrated along its path toward the moon, nothing more than a magnificent jumble of multi-million-dollar junk. It wobbled its way past the moon and then, captured by the lunar gravitational tides, was sucked in to crash mute and useless on the side of the moon unseen by us from the earth.

And yet this man referred proudly to this shot as a great accomplishment on the part of our lunar program.

Sometimes we tend to go overboard in our claims of what we are doing in space. Meteorologists have turned bright red in anger when they heard NASA officials claim that the pictures transmitted to earth by Tiros I provided us with "more information about the weather than we have been able to obtain since the beginning of recorded history . . . approximately six thousand years ago."

It is startling to hear responsible people utter such nonsense. It suggests that we understood nothing of the vast and intricate interplay of forces within the atmosphere. Certainly the Tiros I satellite proved a great boon to the science of meteorology, but the NASA official's claim is unbelievable. Such professional boasting carries over into other fields. A NASA official claimed proudly of the first OSO satellite that it "first functioned in space for only three months and yet, in this short time we have learned nine thousand times more . . . about our sun than we had known prior to its launching."

Such claims are not only ridiculous, but they also mislead people as to the nature of our activities in space. What we are doing in plumbing the depths of space is a wonder in itself; it does not require grandiose nonsense and rampant imagination to lend it dignity or meaning.

Standing above all other space exploration endeavors by either the United States or the Soviet Union is Mariner II—a probe of the planet Venus so spectacularly successful that it merits unrestrained plaudits. The mission of Mariner II was essentially to scan the surface of the planet Venus with instruments in order to obtain the first "close" measurements of the environment surrounding earth's "sister planet," as well as to determine the temperature of the atmosphere, the composition and extent of its cloud cover, and the characteristics of its surface.

For 109 days, Mariner II sailed the reaches of space from earth to Venus, a voyage that reads like the wildest of science fiction. The 447-pound spacecraft journeyed through an environment unknown and incomprehensible to us less than seven years ago. As it drifted away from earth on a trip of 182,000,000 miles, adding its own speed to that of the planets in their orbits about the sun, it fell sunward, away from the earth toward Venus. A NASA official said jubilantly that Mariner II had survived both hardships and spatial conditions that made " 'the perils of Pauline' look like a nursery story." Its intricate and sensitive components faltered more than once in their operation, and scientists for a time feared they had failed altogether. Aboard the spacecraft temperatures soared until they exceeded all design safety limits, and there arose the grim possibility that the batteries might even explode from the heat. And when it reached Venus, the automatic controls which were to turn on the planet-scanning instruments failed to operate. A signal beamed from earth flashed across 36,000,000 miles of space, and the dormant instrument probes of Mariner II stirred to life.

During its journey, the space probe transmitted invaluable data to earth on the intensity of cosmic dust that drifts between the planets. It endured the blasts of solar winds and radiation storms of charged particles that startled scientists with their intensity. It transmitted data on magnetic fields, and by its resistance to solar radiations provided the first accurate readings of temperature levels at varying distances from the sun. For most of its voyage it established new levels of accomplishment in radio transmission and reception across the seas of space.

On December 14, 1962, Mariner II fell past the planet Venus

at a distance of 21,594 miles. This accuracy is spectacular for many reasons. The original plans for Mariner II called for a flyby of the planet at 9,000 miles, instead of 21,594. To reach its planned avenue of flight, the space probe not only had to be launched with incredible accuracy and control, but it also had to perform agile attitude control maneuvers en route to Venus. It then also had to fire a mid-course correction engine which changed its velocity by only a fraction of its original speed—but a fraction that changed what would have been a wide miss into a sensational "hit."

One reason why Mariner II could hardly have been more accurate escaped most students of the first successful interplanetary probe: Scientists did not yet know with any true accuracy the exact distance between the earth and Venus. Mariner II corrected this lack.

Mariner II reached its closest approach to Venus (21,594 miles) at 2:59:28 PM, EST, on December 14, 1962. For forty-two minutes the probe made three complete radiometer studies of the mystery-shrouded planet, and transmitted this data back to earth.

The voice of Mariner II thrilled scientists and laymen alike. It was a melodious tune that varied in pitch and tone according to the particular data secreted within its electronic song. It was not the strident or shrill beeping cries heard from earth-orbiting satellites, but an astonishing melody that one scientist described as "a simple étude on a muted harpsichord."

And it was a melody bursting with unique data. Mariner II taught us that Venus, with a uniform surface temperature of 800 degrees F., could never be host to the dreams of science-fiction writers, who penned stories of a prehistoric swamp world. We learned that a cloud layer 17 miles thick embraces the planet. Mariner II's instruments told us that the cloud layer at its top measures 65 degrees F. below zero; at its base a temperature of 200 degrees F. above zero.

We now hold a picture of the Venusian surface that stands on hard scientific data. It is a world of blistering heat, a rugged terrain, and in all likelihood terribly dry. Scientists are led to believe that parts of the planetary surface may even be molten; the surface temperature is great enough to melt even zinc. Venus is a world of fierce pressures, twenty times greater than that of our atmosphere—294 pounds per square inch on that distant world. Even the cloud cover is astonishing, for it begins at a height of 45 miles, and then extends to its top at 62 miles. Its composition is shrouded in question marks. Mariner II with its limited instruments suggests a cloud layer composed of condensed hydrocarbons, a Venusian "smog."

And were the atmosphere to be transparent rather than opaque, the heavens would be strange indeed. Venus rotates slowly, if at all, hint the instrumented data. From Venus' surface, the stars would seem to stand perfectly still in the night skies. Once every Venusian year (225 Earth days), the sun rises in the west and disappears over the eastern horizon—a time span completely alien to those who live beneath the skies of a rapidly spinning Earth.

NASA Administrator James E. Webb describes the Mariner II study of Venus as

> . . . a significant hour—one in which more may be added to man's knowledge of the planet Venus than has been gained in all the thousands of years of recorded history. By comparing our measurements of the physical characteristics of Venus with those of the Earth, we may open new areas of understanding of our own mother planet. It is an hour, I suspect, which all of us will one day find ourselves sharing with our grandchildren, recalling how we today participated in an historic scientific event, even though we are 36,000,000 miles away.

Mr. Webb could not have said it better.

CHAPTER 6.

CUTTING UP THE BIG SPACE PIE

IN OCTOBER 1958, the National Aeronautics and Space Administration came into being as an executive agency of the Government. The legislation for this agency, the National Aeronautics and Space Act of 1958, directed that:

> ... the general welfare and security of the United States require that adequate provisions be made for aeronautical and space activities. The Congress further declares that such activities shall be the responsibility of, and shall be directed by, a civilian agency exercising control over aeronautical and space activities sponsored by the United States, except that activities peculiar to or primarily associated with the development of weapons systems, military operations, or the defense of the United States (including the research and development necessary to make effective provision for the defense of the United States) shall be the responsibility of, and shall be directed by, the Department of Defense; and that determination as to which such agency has responsibility for and direction of any such activity shall be made by the President. ...

In the President's special message to Congress, April 2, 1958, in which establishment of NASA was recommended, it had been emphasized that:

119

... aeronautical and space science activities sponsored by the United States be conducted under the direction of a civilian agency, except for those projects primarily associated with military requirements. I have reached this conclusion because space exploration holds promise of adding importantly to our knowledge of the Earth, the solar system, and the universe, and because it is of great importance to have the fullest cooperation of the scientific community at home and abroad in moving forward in the fields of space science and technology. Moreover, a civilian setting for the administration of space function will emphasize the concern of our Nation that outer space be devoted to peaceful and scientific purposes.

The official policy of the United States was stated in many ways and by many people. It is perhaps summed up best of all in this proposition stated by the Government when it first undertook to put the space program on a priority basis:

Scientific research has never been amenable to rigorous cost accounting in advance. Nor, for that matter, has exploration of any sort. But if we have learned one lesson, it is that research and exploration have a remarkable way of paying off—quite apart from the fact that they demonstrate that man is alive and insatiably curious. And we all feel richer for knowing what explorers and scientists have learned about the universe in which we live.

The Congress chose to comment as follows on this proposition: *

In this statement there is political support for what the historian, the anthropologist, the psychologist consider to be established fact—that some innate force in the human being makes him *know,* whatever his formal beliefs or whatever his unconscious philosophy, that he *must* progress. Progress is the core of his destiny.

* "The Practical Values of Space Exploration" (Revised August 1961), Staff Study of the Committee on Science and Astronautics, Eighty-seventh Congress, First Session.

This is a concept which, in connection with space exploration, has been recognized for many years. . . .

The human race cannot stand still. It must progress or die out. . . .

All of the glowing predictions being made on behalf of space exploration will not be here tomorrow or the next day. Yet this seems less important than that we recognize the significance of our moment of history.

We may think of that moment as a new age—the age of space and the atom—to follow the historic ages of stone, bronze, and iron. . . .

However we think of it, it is a dawning period and one which—in its scope and potential—promises to dwarf much of what has gone before. Those who have given careful thought to the matter are convinced that while some caution is in order, the new era is not one to be approached with timidity, inhibited imagination or too much convention. Neither is there any point in trying to hold off the tempo of this oncoming age or, in any other way, to evade it. . . .

Those are fine and stirring words. But Dr. Hugh L. Dryden, for nine years the Director of the National Advisory Committee for Aeronautics, and currently the Deputy Administrator of NASA, said simply: "Before Sputnik, if you mentioned the word *space,* your appropriations would be cut for wasting the people's money on foolish things."

Now it is after Sputnik, and sharply conservative estimates are that by the time we reach the year 1970, the United States will have spent in the period 1962-1970 from seventy to one hundred billion dollars on all aspects of our efforts in space.

What has most excited the people of this country and the world, however, has been our effort to send man into space. In this area we were expected to run second-best, and we held to those expectations.

We have attempted to overcome the painful disparities of weight and performance of the opposition's spacecraft and missions by turning to semantics. On April 12, 1961, Yuri Gagarin raced around the planet for history's first manned orbital flight. He pulled this off in a flight of 108 minutes from start to finish, comfortably ensconced within a five-ton vehicle that afforded him sufficient room (were this the purpose on this flight) to get up and move around.

The following month Alan Shepard went into space, and not even the Russians could outperform us in the heady words that described the thrills and wonder of our flight. They ignored the reality of Shepard's flight. His capsule shot up and out of the atmosphere for just about five minutes, as would a fish that leaps out of water and then helplessly tumbles back in again. And we claimed that Shepard had achieved some sort of memorable deed by "flying" his spaceship. In the scant five minutes that he popped like a cork out of the ocean of air, where did Shepard fly? He worked his reaction controls and moved his capsule briefly around its three axes, it is true. But it seems somewhat seedy for a nation such as ours to claim a spectacular distinction through so limited and brief an experiment, if we might dignify this "flying" as such.

The five years in space *after* the orbiting of Sputnik I were for the United States a period of searching and of organizing, more than they were a period of true research beyond the earth. This statement is entirely valid when we realize that virtually everything we have done in space until this time has been accomplished with the same rocket vehicles and equipment that were in existence or under development before the orbiting of Sputnik I on October 4, 1957. Everything, or almost everything, we have accomplished to this moment constitutes a space program with hand-me-down rocket vehicles and supporting equipment.

The National Aeronautics and Space Administration has been in existence since October 1, 1958, approximately one year after the launching of Sputnik I. For some time after its establishment, NASA existed on the basis of handouts, cooperation from military services and other government agencies, and upon the continuation of projects in existence before the passing of the law which created this new civilian space agency.

What is most important for us to consider is not the space effort in the past, but what effect the agency will have upon our future in space. Not too many years from now, most of the rockets with which we stumbled into the space era will be museum pieces, replaced by new vehicles of far greater reliability and performance. But presumably NASA will still be here, and our course into the future will be a matter decided to the greatest extent by this organization which, in its brief lifetime, has expanded with unpredictable speed into one of the most powerful and largest agencies of this nation.

The expansion of NASA has been accompanied by inevitable growing pains. NASA came into existence at a time when the United States reeled before Russian successes in space. This being the case, NASA's early days of existence were certain to be accompanied by the damnation of many critics. To ignore the wounds to our national pride is to be blind, and to ignore the scrabbling for signs of superiority, when few are to be found, is to continue in a state of blindness.

It is not too far in the past to recall the almost constant cries from Washington that belittled the enormous power of Soviet booster rockets—power that by comparison shrank our own satellites to little baubles in the heavens. Dr. Wernher von Braun, in a mood of unhappy resignation, admitted candidly, "Our little Explorers and Vanguards are competing with the Sputniks in spirit only. But in terms of rocket hardware they are no match."

And some inspired but anonymous wag tacked up on the wall, outside the room where the Joint Chiefs of Staff meet in the Pentagon, this notice: "Although the Soviet Union leads the United States in the development of powerful rocket boosters, America maintains its lead in the production of subminiaturized electronic components. Otherwise, it would not have been possible for the

United States to have built a space program so much smaller than the one the Russians have."

As the months passed, it became inevitable that we must discontinue the farce. Inevitable because the United States was finally about to receive more powerful rockets for space use, and the time had come to be boastful of these new rockets and their substantial payloads. On top of this, we found it embarrassing to belittle the need for great boosters in space, because we were asking Congress for literally billions of dollars to rush the development and construction of rocket boosters far bigger than anything the Russians might produce.

It was some time before the truth became known, and scientists and Government authorities finally laid the facts on the line.

In 1960, NASA Administrator Dr. T. Keith Glennan admitted the critical weaknesses of our space efforts because of a lack of powerful boosters and commented:

> This disparity in thrust enables the Soviet Union to undertake very difficult space missions, some of which are completely denied to us today. . . . they are not limited by the weight restrictions we are experiencing. . . . they can avoid the time-consuming business of miniaturization, optimum-packaging, and other weight-saving practices. Moreover, their ability to carry heavy payloads improves the probability of success in any particular experiment because they have adequate weight-carrying margins to permit the employment of redundancy or duplication in many elements of their guidance, control, and communications subsystems.
>
> Urgent and, I believe, effective efforts are being made, both by NASA and by the Department of Defense, to develop a family of launch vehicle systems that will correct this imbalance.

The following year (1961), Dr. Hugh Dryden cut things just a bit finer in his explanation to a Congressional Committee:

... we have guidance equipment which to the best of our knowledge is as accurate as the Russians'. Because of the limits on the weight of vehicles we can launch we have not been able to use it. ... In the cases where the Russians have exhibited instrumentation and equipment to us, it has not been highly miniaturized. And they don't need to, with the weights that they have available.

I have no doubt about the ability of the Russians to miniaturize equipment if they want to. They just haven't had to. They have had so much surplus weight that they just didn't have to do it.

The most chronic of the growing pains of NASA has been its struggle to establish beyond question in the public mind that the United States ventures into space only for the sake of peace and good will among all men. This, more than all others, is a task so staggering that NASA's efforts in this direction seem relegated to failure even before they begin.

The problem is inherent in the manner in which the United States first approached the whole area of exploring space. Since the great body of scientists in this country were sure to dissociate themselves from space programs before Sputnik I, our entire *civilian* stake in exploring space was relegated to the woefully inadequate Project Vanguard. Our posture in space was to be civilian, and there were to be no overtones of the military to muddy up the shining crystal of pure science.

This move cracked wide open the solid front of civilian activities in space. The basis for the Vanguard's first-stage booster rocket was the Viking research vehicle, specifically not a missile. But Viking was a Navy project, conceived and developed entirely by the United States Navy. The engine for the Vanguard first-stage, to be developed by General Electric, was a development from the Hermes A-3 guided missile which, in turn, was a test series of rockets picked up from German missile research in World War II. The second stage of Vanguard came from the Aerobee series of high-altitude research rockets. Again, these were not missiles, but they were the products of both the Air Force and the Navy.

It is difficult to see exactly how this country, by the mumbo-jumbo of assigning "civilian names" to our space activities, could ignore the realities of developing the Vanguard booster vehicle.

After the first two Russian satellites swept around the planet, while Vanguard's initial exploration of space was limited to the first six inches above the sands of Cape Canaveral, the Washington scene became desperate. What we did was to turn frantically to the military to get a satellite up—and be damned as to what kind of rocket we used to do the job.

The old Redstone with its upper-stage clusters of solid-propellant rockets was dragged from its storage hangar and rushed back to Cape Canaveral, and on January 31, 1958, we were finally in the game. Of course, the Redstone had been ready since 1956 to do the same job it did in 1958, but in those days Redstone was a military untouchable.

In this fashion we staggered into the space age. A year after the orbiting of the first Russian satellite, NASA was in business. And one of NASA's first tasks *was* to paint new names on the old military missiles in order that they might be classified as nonmilitary, civilian boosters.

Some day the students of the beginning of the space age will be driven mad by the nomenclature of Explorer I and the subsequent series of satellites which were kicked into orbit by military missiles-turned-boosters. The Government, in a move right out of *Alice in Wonderland,* proclaimed to the world that the launching of our first satellite was our contribution to the IGY, and as such represented America's nonmilitary, untainted, civilian steps into space.

The problem blossomed to uncomfortable proportions when NASA began a systematic program of flinging satellites into orbit and dispatching payloads outward to the moon. The problem became strained for the reason that all the boosters were those same old military rockets—Jupiter-C, Juno II, Thor-Able (which forms the basis for Thor-Ablestar, Thor-Delta, Thor-Epsilon, et al.), Atlas, Atlas-Agena, and others under development.

The breaking point seemed at hand when representatives of NASA reacted in a huff to any description of a NASA rocket as a missile. "It's *not* a missile," they cried, "it's a *booster!*" The game of "change the name" was being played in earnest.

It must be noted that the rockets were modifications of missiles and included a fair number of vehicles already assigned by the military services to their own space experiments.

Not only was this embarrassing to the "pure civilian" concept of space exploration, but many of the NASA missions stemmed from existing military projects which, by the sorcery of hastily applied new designations, somehow became civilian. Passive and active communications satellites, navigation satellites, radiation satellites, lunar probes, and the whole vast array of civilian satellite projects were almost inclusively existing military programs prior to the creation by the Congress of NASA.

Project Mercury, despite all that has been said of this civilian man-in-space program, was an existing, working, military effort long before NASA came upon the scene. The powerful Saturn booster rocket, the Centaur booster, the huge F-1 engine of 1,500,000 pounds thrust—these and many others were existing military projects which fell under NASA jurisdiction shortly after this agency was established. NASA had no choice but to emphasize again and again that it was a civilian agency; Congress had so decreed. What muddled the situation, and painted a picture of the United States as trying desperately to avoid reality, is that we seemed to regard anything military as something with which no respectable scientist wished to be connected.

From this stream of conflicting statements and impressions there arose a hue and cry familiar to Washington, the battle of the giants as both civilian and military officials scrapped among each other to cut up the big space pie. Washington has seen so many of these struggles in the past that it was quite natural to assume a raging conflict between the military and NASA as to what organization should really control space.

The gist of the argument is that the military claimed that jurisdiction should rightfully belong to the military structure of the country, while NASA claimed that the job, as spelled out by the President and by the Congress, was a civilian effort. In this melee, NASA not only sustained its position, but grew in leaps and bounds to a huge organization wielding billions of dollars annually in industrial and research contracts.

This has all been rather puzzling simply because there has never really been any controversy about what type of organization should carry out the bulk of America's activities in space. But the uproar from Washington and the false conclusions drawn by the press painted an entirely different picture. There is controversy, to be sure, about whether or not NASA in its space activities, as separate and distinct from those of the military organizations, might overshadow so greatly the defense needs of the country that we will allow the necessary research to produce weapons systems for space to flounder. The argument, then, is more one of definitions of control of research areas than it is of making a clear decision as to whether or not America is a civilian or a military space power.

The truth is that we are both. The unfortunate harping on the civilian nature of our program, however, has built the false conception that we must at all costs keep the military out of space. The conclusion has been drawn that if we do not muzzle military space activities, we are dooming ourselves to intensive battles beyond the earth. By this reasoning, the earth is therefore declared fit for the horror of war, but space is to be kept clean and pure.

The military organization, by virtue of its mission, must investigate any and all possibilities of space vehicles or systems employed militarily against the United States. In this area we have failed to make the distinctions needed to satisfy both the mandate of the Congress and assurance of defense for the country.

CHAPTER **7.**

THE VOTES WERE FOR NASA

DURING April and May of 1958, the Select Committee on Astronautics and Space Exploration of the Eighty-fifth Congress held extensive hearings on the subject of this country's future plans and activities in the fields of astronautics and space exploration. The Committee made this careful introduction to its hearings:

> We plan to conduct these hearings openly. The scope and detail of their disclosures will be limited only by actual questions of national security. To work in any other way would do a disservice to the country. The problems that face the Congress and the Nation in matters of outer space development are so immense and so critical that they must have the help of an informed public opinion.
>
> In space exploration, and the scientific breakthrough it implies, we are beginning an era of discovery literally as far-reaching as the discovery of our own continent. It is necessary that each broad step in this discovery be made with the American people being as fully informed as possible.
>
> ... The immediate problem is obvious. We see another nation of great potentiality, militant and competitive, which has already made the first advances in the mastery of outer space. We cannot stand by and watch this nation make that mastery complete. As Lt. General James M. Gavin, the

Army's recently retired Chief of Research put it: "If they (that is, the Russians) surpass us in technology in the years ahead, there is little doubt who will determine the future of the world."

... We have many questions before us. Shall the new Agency be controlled by military men or by civilians? Can a civilian organization look after military needs as well? How big—and how limited—will be the new Agency's jurisdiction? Will it act on space problems alone?

Through all these considerations we must also continually balance two things: the immediate emergency needs—the long-range possibilities and their cost. We must also look at the other dark side of the coin. What would Soviet ascendancy in this field mean, to our safety, if not our existence as a Nation?

These are some of the questions which we hope to clarify during our hearings. In keeping with the urgency of this investigation, we are calling no witness who is not absolutely essential to it. Since the first advances in space exploration were made under the direction of the military, our witnesses will include some of those who have been most intimately concerned with the present space plans. . . .

The following statements were made by witnesses who had military backgrounds, or who were involved with military programs.

Dr. Wernher von Braun, Director, Development Operations Division, Army Ballistic Missile Agency:

The very scope of the exploration of outer space is so vast as simply to preclude its being the byproduct or fallout of anything. We can meet this challenge only if we appreciate and respect the magnitude of this task and discontinue our unfortunate practice of supporting only such research and development that serves immediate military objectives. . . . we must carefully retain the present atmosphere of free and full exchange of information in order to avoid costly duplication of effort and to provide for mutual assistance between teams. Also, our scientists should be free to pursue their efforts without continual worry about a program cancelation putting them out of business and thus destroying the team they have built up.

Major General John B. Medaris, Commanding General, United States Army Ordnance Command:

I have at no time proposed that this should be a military operation, controlled and directed by a military man. . . .

There is an attempt to spell out the different areas of responsibility as between NASA and the Department of Defense. The only difficulty lies in the fact that there is going to be a considerable shadow zone to be resolved, but certainly it does not provide any basis which would lead to a, shall we say, kind of interbureau struggle of who is boss.

Lt. General James M. Gavin (Ret.), former Deputy Chief, Office of Research and Development, U.S. Army:

. . . I am thinking along the lines that we have developed the Atomic Energy Commission because I do believe that the civilian application of the space program will be far more important than the military. So it should be under a civilian agency. Furthermore, you would disassociate it from service problems, service budgeting problems which can become very serious in peace.

Rear Admiral Hyman G. Rickover, Assistant Chief, Bureau of Ships, for Nuclear Propulsion, Department of the Navy:

I definitely believe that the organization should be under civilian control. . . .

There is today a complete blurring of identity between military and civilian matters. War is now not a matter for the military alone. I am sure you are fully aware that the military is merely the cutting edge of the sword. . . .

Furthermore, if we are ever to have peace in this tortured

world of ours, we must make a beginning—we must get away from the purely military applications of space. We must recognize that the marriage of the military and science is proceeding too fully and too strongly; we must attempt to stop this tendency and instead emphasize the peaceful applications of science.

In response to a question about the nature of clearly defined authority for our space program as it existed in 1958, Admiral Rickover responded by stating:

. . . we never put anyone in charge. I defy you to find anyone in the Federal Government that has any final responsibility for anything, a clear-cut responsibility. I know that Members of Congress have tried for many years to find such an individual, but you cannot locate him. Certainly not in Washington.

How can you possibly have real responsibility, particularly in the military where the people keep on changing all the time? So if something goes wrong, the man occupying the desk at the time can say, "Well, the man that was here before me started it—he is responsible." And the man who started it can say, "I left the job before it was finished, so I'm not responsible." This freedom from responsibility is a marvelous invention.

So we in the military have a "union" too. This is our union—that we are not around long enough to be responsible for anything. You must have responsibility if you are going to get a job done. And once you give a man responsibility you have got to see to it that he is not bothered too much by the pure administrators who are always making sure that the many minor rules and regulations are carried out exactly. . . .

I would like to see space considered as belonging to all nations, just as the high seas do. You cannot separate its military aspects from the purely scientific, the peaceful aspects, sir. They are intertwined. You cannot make a real distinction.

Dr. James H. Doolittle, Chairman, National Advisory Committee for Aeronautics; Lt. General, USAF (Ret.):

> ... our national space effort must be under civil direction insofar as the very important, nonmilitary aspects of the program are concerned, with the necessary proviso that there must be effective cooperation and coordination between the civil space work and the military space work.
>
> From my years in uniform, I know that the military space projects will benefit greatly from the work of the NASA. It would be difficult, or impossible, for the Nation to fully accomplish its major space objectives if the program were under strictly military control. Direction and leadership of the program must be the responsibility of a civilian agency as provided in the bill.

This has been and still remains the consensus. The military—individually and, it appears, collectively—exhibit an overwhelming support for the national space agency under the direct control of and operated as a civilian organization. There arises from the foregoing, of course, the inevitable question. So much for the sentiments, but has this civilian agency received the support and willing cooperation of the military services?

In the spring of 1960, General Schriever explained to a Congressional Committee:

> Our military and civilian operations complement each other. Both must be pursued with imagination and vigor in the national interest. In such pursuit, close cooperation between the existing space agencies—primarily the Air Force, which now has responsibility for military booster development, systems integrations, and launching operations—and the National Aeronautics and Space Agency, which is responsible for civilian space boosters and other civilian space activities, is not only desirable, but mandatory. Only by such cooperation can our Nation muster the best in the way of brains and facilities and utilize them to the fullest. This kind of cooperation does

prevail today between the Air Force and the National Aeronautics and Space Agency.

In August 1962, General Schriever commented further:

> ...NASA is not...sufficient unto itself. The military services budget a lot of money that supports the NASA programs.
>
> For example, the Air Force budgets for the operation of the Atlantic Missile Range, which supports NASA. We do not get any money from NASA on this.
>
> The Navy has ships at sea that support the Mercury shots. NASA does not pay for them.
>
> The fact is that NASA is dependent upon a lot of agencies to carry out its responsibilities. It is never going to budget for all of the funds required and then pass them out to people that do the various supporting tasks. The problem is too complicated.

The 1960 Report of the Secretary of the Air Force takes pains to detail the extensive supporting activities of the Air Force for the other military services and for NASA. The extent of this in-house integration and cooperation is not as well known as it should be, for it denotes the kind of cooperation we have long clamored for in the best interests of the country. In addition to its own programs for Midas, Samos and Discoverer satellites, the Air Force, to support the Navy's Transit satellite effort and the Army's communications satellites, supplied boosters, integrated payloads into the systems, launched, tracked, recorded data, and otherwise supported these elaborate and extensive efforts.

In its program of supporting NASA, the Air Force supplied the boosters that sent Tiros, Explorer, Pioneer and other satellites into orbit and outward from the earth in deep-space probes. The Report notes specifically that "for NASA's Mercury project, the Air Force furnished fourteen Atlas boosters, launching facilities, and technical assistance. In addition, the Air Force conducted balloon tests for NASA and provided various types of training equipment for the Mercury astronauts."

Dr. Glennan, the NASA Administrator, confirmed this level of cooperation when he testified to the Congress:

> Almost all of the biomedical requirements of Project Mercury have been supplied by the Department of Defense. This assistance has been in the form of direct assignment of military personnel to NASA's Space Task Group and in making available facilities and other personnel for consultation and support.
> . . . The undertaking of Project Mercury would have been substantially more costly and its operation may possibly have been delayed without biomedical support by the military services.

In 1960, General Thomas D. White, Air Force Chief of Staff, carefully outlined the official Air Force policy with his remarks: "I am convinced that one of the major long-range elements of the Air Force future lies in space. It is also obvious that NASA will play a large part in the national effort in this direction and, moreover, inevitably will be associated, if not eventually combined with the military. It is perfectly clear to me that particularly in these formative years the Air Force must, for its own good as well as for national interest, cooperate to the maximum extent with NASA, to include the furnishing of key personnel even at the expense of some Air Force dilution of technical talent."

In the following year, the Congress called upon General White for further amplification of this statement. The General replied: ". . . I want to make it crystal clear that the policy is we will cooperate with NASA—and to the very limit of our ability and even beyond, to the extent of some risk to our own programs. The Air Force will cooperate and will support all reasonable key personnel requests made on it by NASA."

This was the picture. The Congress of the United States, in its desire to best develop the country's resources and means to exploit our capabilities in the space era, had established a civilian organization to fulfill national objectives, while assigning to the military singular responsibility for military space applications. In order for the civilian agency (NASA) to function properly, it required the extensive cooperation of and coordination with the military services, notably the Air Force.

Unfortunately, there was no guarantee that the agency as established would not interfere by virtue of its activities with the country's critical need to assure its military defense capabilities in space, or that the agency would move quickly enough or in the right directions to assure the technological leadership of the United States in its competition with the USSR.

CHAPTER 8.

WHO'S MINDING THE STORE?

SINCE the United States embarked upon the civilian exploration of space this question has haunted our Congressional leaders, bedeviled budgetary meetings in Washington, troubled military officials, and entertained the Soviet Union.

It went unanswered in the days of establishing the National Aeronautics and Space Administration, when the Congress clearly drew the line by authorizing the civilian agency to manage the majority of our affairs in space. At that time, in 1958, the Congressional recognition of the need for military space developments was expressed in the NASA Act with the directive: "Activities peculiar to or primarily associated with the development of weapons systems, military operations, or the defense of the United States . . . shall be the responsibility of, and shall be directed by, the Department of Defense."

This was fine as far as it went, which was hardly beyond the partially opened door to military space research and development. The wording was vulnerable to misinterpretation. Such, in fact, was the case, and in proposals and amendments in 1960 and 1961 by the Congress to the act creating NASA, the Congress strengthened its original directive by adding: "The Department of Defense shall undertake such activities in space, and such research and development connected therewith, as may be necessary for the defense of the United States."

Still the words remained open to misunderstanding and misinterpretation. The confusion and the indecision in the attempts to evaluate the military role in space revolved about questions of what shall, and what shall not, the Air Force do in space. These are questions that do not strike at the heart of the problem. The gnawing core of concern is the question of how operations in space by the Russians will affect us.

This is the gist of the concept, but it is seemingly an elusive one to those officials responsible for deciding to what extent authority and funds should be provided to the prime agency responsible for military space developments. And what only confuses the issue further is that, when pressed for specific programs, the military themselves cannot clearly identify future needs.

Despite this lack of a well-established, easily defended future military mission in space, as defined by budgeting for a specific weapons system, the military fears of weakness are well grounded. The problem is not peculiar to the arena of space. It is caused by the same myopia which through the decades has forced us to stumble awkwardly in our predictions of new weapons, and our progression from one outmoded system to another. Most of all, we have been hopelessly inept at predicting the weapon that a potential enemy might employ against us.

Our record in World War I, in terms of planning capably for the new element of combat in the air, is one of the blackest pages in our history. With acid kindness the French described the air fleet with which we ventured into that war as "a magnificent retrospective museum." There could be no denial that we had earned the comment, for these aircraft were fit only to be thrown into the bonfire so that they might not kill off the few pilots we had. The aerial conflict in Europe had raged for thirty-two months, and our keen observations of this battle in the skies produced a total of only 55 airplanes that could even get off the ground. We failed to produce a single airplane of our own design and manufacture that was fit for combat. Lt. Colonel H. A. Toulmin, Jr., the Air Historian, reported of our Air Service program in France that the whole thing was "a practical failure; was facing the possibilities of disaster . . . and was faced with moral and mental disintegration and disarrangement, which was insidiously wrecking the very integrity and the morale of the entire service."

Our attempts to supply leadership, production, training and combat quality for aerial battle in World War I failed to progress beyond a level of squalid inefficiency and outright criminal negligence of duty. Of our conduct in France, Colonel Hiram Bingham concluded with obvious dismay that this "was the worst page in the history of the Air Service."

Even this unfortunate page in the history of the nation that gave birth to the first controlled flight by man in a heavier-than-air machine failed to provide a lesson to the men who would chart our future course. The Congressional hearings of the past bulge with the accumulated views not only of outright opponents to airpower, but also of members of the Air Service itself who willingly acceded to the "obvious realization" that only the infantry could ever provide a decisive force in war.

This may explain why we entered World War II with airplanes so antiquated and inferior that, for the most part, they were slaughtered by the opposition. Our history books record with commendable patriotism that we shipped hundreds of warplanes to England to assist that beleaguered stronghold in its fight against the Luftwaffe; few accounts include the dismal fact that the British never uncrated these fighters, but shipped the machines to Africa where they might be used against equipment on the ground.

In the period between wars, not even the most outspoken of the architects of the air could free themselves of the ingrained idea that wars must always and ultimately be resolved "hand to hand."

It is not widely known—and it would be denied by those not fully aware of the details—that even Billy Mitchell subscribed generally to this concept. Despite his ceaseless insistence upon the role that military airpower must inevitably play in future conflicts, Mitchell in 1921 did not hesitate to admit, "The ultimate defense of a country depends on its manpower. This means the infantry, with its auxiliaries, fighting on the ground as man to man; and everything, whether it be in the air or on the water, must be organized with a view to assisting this human force."

It has often been claimed that the space age is so new, so vast and so different from anything that we have done before that we cannot turn to the past in order to profit from errors we may have committed in prior years. But this is to claim that we cannot profit from experience, or benefit from our mistakes, and the claim is ridiculous from any point of view.

A parallel to our current dilemma has occurred in many ways and to different degrees in past activities, but it took a German air force officer to express the case in the clearest of terms. General Koller, the last chief of the German Air Staff in World War II, warned:

> The Air Force must be allowed to move its wings freely and must be relieved of the ballast of ground and naval forces. Future supreme commanders must have Air Force officers in the decisive positions, men who can think in terms of the world and who have a wide horizon. Every soldier generally thinks only as far as the radius of his branch of service and only as quickly as he can move with his weapons.

Amplifying the statements he made in 1945, General Koller concluded: "We have been beaten and eliminated, we have nothing more to say. But it will be interesting to watch the development of the Great Powers and the battle of wits. *Will it be as it always has been, that they all, every one of them, will not learn from the past and will continue to make the old mistakes again and again?*"

This is precisely the problem we face—or rather, that a limited number of people in this country are facing. It is distressing but accurate to report that there has sprung up in our political and space camps a strange aversion to the "military in space." It is as if by the magic of eloquence in the United Nations or in Government proclamations we could prevent the spread of earthly conflicts to the vacuum beyond the world. It is not so astonishing that this is the hope. It is incredible to see that this is the belief. And these people are permitting a dangerous precedent. They are willing to gamble that they are right, and that all the lessons and the experience of the past are, miraculously, erased by our movement into a new environment.

From this quasi-religious conviction that we shall keep wars from soiling the space environment, there has come into existence a determined effort to restrict even the vitally needed research of the military to determine with some accuracy in what areas we may be faced with spaceborne weapons of overwhelming power.

Dr. C. C. Furnas, Chancellor of the University of Buffalo, and former Assistant Secretary of Defense for Research and Development, foresaw this issue years ago. In 1958 he gave warning to this danger when he presented the question:

> If this new agency, the NASA, is established, how far should the Military Establishment be permitted to conduct or support research of more or less fundamental character in the general field of space technology? I can see some very old arguments being dusted off and put out on display. There are those who feel that the military organization should stick very closely to its knitting and only develop military hardware; that it should not broaden its operations to encompass anything resembling fundamental explorations. There is still considerable feeling that it is not appropriate for the military to dabble in "scientific toys."
>
> I feel that such arguments get the cart before the horse. If there is even a small probability that military weapons systems now or in the future are going to need some block of funda-

mental scientific information, which is not now being adequately sought for in some other quarter, then it is incumbent upon the Military Establishment to see that that general area is being adequately explored. Further, anyone who is involved in the development of military weapons systems can foresee the need for applied research activities and even component developments which are certainly going to be needed several years hence. . . .

This matter requires the understanding afforded by the men who have been closest to its problems. In 1960, Brigadier General Robert C. Richardson, III, then Chief, Long-Range Objectives Group, Plans and Programs, US Air Force, enlarged upon the theme set forth by Dr. Furnas. General Richardson warned:

> Future military hardware is relatively predictable by comparison with future concepts. The weapons we can have at any time will depend on the emphasis given to research and development. Except for unanticipated breakthroughs, we can fairly accurately estimate the type and performance of the hardware that we can hope to have for the next ten to fifteen years. Changes in concepts, on the other hand, are not as easy to predict or to come by. While generally triggered by changes in hardware, they originate in assumptions and opinions rather than in projection of tangible, technical facts. . . .
>
> When we reflect upon military history, it seems to have been easier to change military hardware than military ideas and organizations. For example, the last U.S. Cavalry charge was purportedly in the Spanish-American War, yet the cavalry was not disbanded by the United States until we were in World War II some forty-one years later. Concepts, force requirements and organizations have not kept abreast of technology.

It is not difficult to see the same pattern of the past being re-enacted in the present. The arguments of civilian versus military control of the national venture into space has obscured the intrinsic national need. It is not enough to achieve unlimited technological stature in space (and NASA by no means assures this or offers conclusive evidence that it will assure this goal) if in the process of "keeping the military in their place" we compromise the nation's ability to defend itself from attack through this new medium.

History to date has been a matter of gradual and defined progression, and until the present era Time has been a comfortable and constantly available ally. Now it is necessary to assume, because it is inevitable, that great and profound changes will occur in the normal course of events.

We must adopt a fresh and realistic approach. The direction of events, whether or not we are willing to recognize the facts of life, has been removed from the hands of the planners. The transitions from foot infantry with hand-to-hand weapons to armored columns, from battleships to carriers, from tactical airpower to global air strike capability, have all been gradual. It is difficult yet imperative to realize that the next change may come about so swiftly and so unannounced that we will be caught entirely off balance. If we do not recognize this need for a new and vital means of preparing for future eventualities, then we may yet find ourselves facing a whole new age, armed not only with obsolete weapons but, what is worse, with antiquated concepts of the events of that new world.

These leading military and industrial officials, as well as individuals with military backgrounds or whose activities closely relate to military affairs, who testified before the Congress as to the need for the civilian space agency also took particular pains to caution the Congress that such an agency posed a grave danger to the nation.

The danger was not in the structure, the purpose, or the leadership of the agency, but that our political leaders and the public might assume that the civilian space agency in its efforts could meet almost all of the defense interests of this nation in space. This is what seems in fact to have happened, and the misgivings suffered by those responsible for the national security arise from our present situation, in which the United States is courting a critical, perhaps fatal, imbalance in building space capabilities.

The Congress has allowed, and even specified in law, a space development requirement by the Department of Defense. It is, unfortunately, far from a statement of intent. The proper interpretation of that law is to the effect that the military may conduct research and development in space to assure the US that we are not forfeiting our means of defense.

The warnings supplied in 1958 are clear. Dr. Wernher von Braun emphasized these facts:

> The exploration of space has become technically possible now due to the general progress made in the art of building large missiles. This has led us into a situation which is in some respects similar to that of shipping shortly after the invention of the compass.
>
> All of a sudden it became then possible to leave the shores and cross the oceans and explore distant lands. Claims were staked out and trade routes developed, but very soon thereafter the nations sponsoring such exploration felt that they had to protect their expeditions and foreign footholds and trade lanes and this brought frigates and caravels and finally full-fledged navies into the act.
>
> Very much in the same way, I think, in the long run we cannot hope to pursue a purely scientific or economical program of exploration of outer space without a minimum of military backing. Let us not forget that the Spanish did not and could not only send cargo ships over to Central and South America to explore and exploit and colonize these lands, they soon found it necessary to build their armada to protect this operation.
>
> Exploration of new lands, whether in Central America or on the moon, should be a double-barreled approach. The scientific exploration comes first, but the military protection of it must go hand-in-hand with it.

...history is full of examples that prove that one-sided unilateral statements by any one nation on some principle such as the freedom of the seas are rather meaningless unless that nation has a navy to back up that statement in case of trouble.

I think the same can be said about our forthcoming ventures into outer space. I am all for a universally accepted rule that outer space is just as free as the open ocean, but I think unless we as a nation or the United Nations have some means to back this rule up, it would remain a very meaningless, empty statement.

... the question of whether we or another nation has control of the spaces around the earth will have a very great impact on our military position on the earth itself. In other words, space superiority, control of the spaces around the earth, will soon be just as important as air superiority is today.

In his appearance before the Congressional Committee, Major General John B. Medaris was queried as to his thoughts on whether "space exploration should be a pure civilian scientific venture over which the military should have no control." General Medaris made it specifically clear that he did not favor a military rule of the missions to be conducted by the NASA, and then he cut sharply to the very crux of the whole question so disturbing to the Congress and the nation at large: "The point is not whether space exploration should or should not be a pure civilian venture; the point is that historically no nation has ever laid claim to anything and held it without military support."

General Medaris than cautioned the Committee that the problem certain to arise in the future was the dividing line between necessary "civilian" and "military" space efforts, and that:

Neither this bill nor succeeding events can completely define in all cases where this division point is. Now, if it develops in such a way that there is a very closely knit cooperative effort between this agency and the Department of Defense, and a mutually supporting arrangement, so that there is no quarreling or quibbling over the shadow zones in a thousand places, if it is a question of where it is going and into what it is going to develop, then there is no reason why it could not be an effective answer.

On the other hand, as I say, the only things that trouble me are the fact that I find it very difficult in my own mind, with assurance, to divide out the scientific, the peaceful, and the military, in terms of any kind of intensive forward research. This does not mean that this kind of organization cannot do it effectively. It means that it is going to require the close cooperation of well-intentioned people. . . .

It is not a question of who is on top and who is on the bottom. We in the military are dedicated to the principle of civilian control of our military affairs. We believe that is a proper and essential basic part of our system of government.

We have no quarrel with that. What worries me . . . is that it has been difficult in the past under military programs, recognized as weapons programs, to be able to justify and secure the funds and support for the type of forward-reaching research which in its turn will develop new weapons systems.

I am somewhat fearful that the more the scientific and military are divided, the more difficult it will be for us to really go forward in the research area in those things that must be done now if the next generation of military weapons will be as good as those which we may meet on some field of battle. This is my fear.

The hard core of scientific research came under the scrutiny of Dr. Simon Ramo, Executive Vice President, Ramo-Wooldridge Corporation of California:

Research in medicine, biology, nuclear physics and other physical and life sciences all promise benefits and can all be classed as vital in the long run to our security. . . . If all such basic research is controlled by the Department of Defense, it is justifiable to fear that we may not explore sufficiently the longer range aspects of science. In this sense, it is reasonable to consider a separate civilian agency to direct and sponsor nonmilitary space research. But this will work to the detriment of the Nation if, in the process of trying to separate pure research in space from research and development necessary to insure military space capability, proper consideration is not given to the extremely important connection between these two aspects of space. No matter what basic space research the new agency may carry on, no arbitrary rule should prevent the Department of Defense from engaging in the space research it may deem essential to sound advanced military developments. In other words, the new space agency should not be thought of as having a monopoly on space research.

Roy W. Johnson, Director, Advanced Research Projects Agency (ARPA), Department of Defense:

... I believe a civilian astronautics agency should be created with its own funds for use in pursuing its programs. However, military programs already demand the use of outer space for many uses for the protection of our country.

The legislation setting up a civilian group should not be worded that it may be construed to mean that the military uses of space are to be limited by a civilian agency. This could be disastrous. It behooves the writers of this legislation to state positively this freedom and without equivocation.

... as this program accelerates, there will be daily decisions that must be made, almost hourly decisions. I have seen in the last sixty days, the tempo increasing. I think that, actually, the time will come, if we go this road, where you may have to have a vice president in charge of space to be so knowledgeable of what is military and what is not military that he can be sitting making daily decisions every hour on the hour. I cannot conceive of any other way to answer this sort of thing if there is going to be a constant difference of opinion. And I can see these differences of opinion increasing as we in the Department of Defense do more military-science exploration.

I think, if you tell the Department of Defense that in military science you are limited to other fields than this, we are making a mistake, because I believe Russia is not inhibited by demanding that there be a military weapons system conceivable and immediately ahead before they explore military sciences.

Mr. Johnson, as subsequent events were to emphasize, proved a prophet with honor.

The United States moved into the space competition between itself and the USSR falsely secure in the conviction that although we had trailed in the opening phases of space exploration, our inherent superiority would regain quickly for us any temporary disadvantages.

It was, in 1958, a grievous error.

It is, in 1963, an error rapidly mushrooming into a national miscalculation that may cost us dearly in the coming years.

Perhaps General Koller, from the acute clarity of vision that overwhelming defeat brings, was right when he said we "will not learn from the past and will continue to make the old mistakes again and again."

CHAPTER **9.**

STORM WARNINGS

IT is not a simple matter to find a clear definition of the problems that concern the United States and its military capabilities in space. Many a solution has been offered in terms of the necessity to control the "high ground" of any battlefield, but this seems to stretch a point in terms of warfare on the earth, and within its ocean of air, as related to the peculiar means of locomotion beyond the atmosphere. An airplane within our air ocean is still the master of its direction; it can change altitude and heading with relative ease, it can circle a given area, and has, in short, an extraordinary range of flexibility. It endures certain limitations imposed by the amount of fuel that may be carried; but so long as its source of power functions it may be sustained, maneuvered and easily controlled.

Not so the spacecraft. The mechanics of space flight are now, and for a long time to come will be, a colossal problem to the military. This is not to claim that efficient and greatly destructive use cannot, and will not, be carried out with space vehicles. However, the mechanics of space flight demand movement at tremendous speeds or, at the least, movement dictated by a precision balance between centrifugal force and the awesome tug of terrestrial gravity.

Being able to move a spacecraft about its three axes doesn't even belong in the same breath as the movement of an aircraft in virtually any direction. A spacecraft in orbit may tumble, roll, gyrate, fly backwards, or straight up and down, and its orbit will remain entirely unaffected. Movement into and away from a specific orbit entails the most critical of computations and the most exacting of power applications. Getting there "fustest with the mostest" may be the creed of the intercontinental ballistic missile, but not necessarily that of other space weapons systems.

These are the negative approaches to the problem and the arguments used in defense of the "keep the military out of space—besides, you can't fight a war up there" stand. Still there are meaningful dangers and promises of military developments in the space systems. Some of the more obvious already are known to us. These include the ICBM itself which is, from any viewpoint, a weapon that spends most of its brief lifetime sustained by centrifugal force in its ballistic arc.

The reconnaissance and detection satellites have received and deserved headline space in our newspapers, to say nothing of the billions of dollars already expended in their development. Specifically, one is the Midas satellite (Missile Defense Alarm System) which uses a battery of infrared sensors to detect ascending rocket exhausts and thermonuclear fireballs—as well as, in its more sophisticated versions, being able to seek out through heat radiated in the infrared, the location of factories, jet airfields, and other sites of interest to target planners. In its ultimate form the Midas system is to have at least twelve satellites orbiting the earth along a polar track—that is, from north to south so that it encompasses the entire planet in its global sweep, and manages to bring the Soviet Union and its satellite areas completely under bright-eyed surveillance from above.

Midas is not a weapon with which we can hurl destructive packages at the enemy, nor is this the intention. It is, as one Air Force officer wryly termed the system, a "spaceborne burglar alarm for which we may one day be deeply grateful." If successful, and Midas is receiving the earnest attention of some of the best scientists in this country, this particular system may assure a constant surveillance and alarm system of Russian ICBM launching sites.

Equally as valuable to our future is the partner to Midas, the satellite system known as Samos. This is another globe-circling agent with the means of ferreting out vital information about the Soviet Union's capacity to wage war against the United States.

Samos is a collection of space-going cameras whose capability is a military secret. Suffice it to say that the U-2 performed miracles of reconnaissance from the upper atmosphere. From heights of even one hundred thousand feet the heavy cameras packed into the U-2's belly stripped away the opaque protection of the USSR provided by its powerful anti-aircraft defense systems.

The success of the U-2—attested to by the furor of the Soviet Union's reaction—only puts deeper emphasis on the need to continue this line of endeavor. Specifically, we are trying our damnedest to learn as much as we possibly can about Russian target locations—airfields, dams, launching sites, factories—which would be invaluable if the Soviet Union waged war.

Like Midas, Samos is not classified as an "offensive weapon." It carries no bombs or guns. It is a battery of eyes contained in a single package far above the earth, ghosting silently through space at 17,000 miles per hour, hunting out details of Russian military-industrial strength.

Midas and Samos, to date, have not suffered for lack of financial or national industrial-scientific priority. These were programs launched well before Sputnik I entered the scene, and they result from the ability of the Atlas plus an Agena upper stage to boost heavy loads with great precision into desired orbits. This is assuming a capability that is nothing less than tremendous—for it is to be done on the basis of automatic and remote systems. It cannot be performed on the basis of hoping for one shot in four. This is a military system and in a military system reliability is the key to successful performance. The most dazzling space success, if it cannot be repeated on demand, is nothing more than a fluke which cannot be relied upon.

Through the building stages of the Air Force's development programs in space, the sustaining structure has been a project known as Discoverer. This involves a two-stage rocket vehicle, comprised of a modified Thor intermediate-range ballistic missile as the first-stage booster, and an Agena rocket for the second stage. It is one of the most remarkable machines ever built for the development of reliable capabilities in space, and it is without the kudos we give to programs laden with promotion and publicity.

The Discoverer series will never establish any weight-lifting records in space, and this has never been its intention—although there is nothing wrong with payloads of 1,200 pounds being placed in orbit with a timetable regularity that is difficult to believe in our present day of boosters exploding or failing in their missions. We have fired not several, but several dozen of the Thor-Agena vehicles. In its role as a military booster the Discoverer series of satellites has broken down the walls to successful and systematic utilization of space vehicles as reliable systems.

To meet the stringent needs of the military—and it should be noted that military satellite needs far exceed those of scientific research vehicles—it must be possible, first of all, to stabilize an orbiting satellite in terms of attitude. The satellite must be commanded to orient one particular end toward the earth and this means a constantly changing attitude control that uses the horizon of the earth as its source of reference. This is operated either on the basis of electronic memory units or command signals from the ground, which "lock" the satellite in position or perform required maneuvers.

It is necessary for the propulsion system of the Discoverer satellite, which includes payload and booster frame as an integral unit, to exhibit a capability for several engine ignitions and cutoffs while in orbit. A multistart capability in orbit is the kind of a problem that will send engineers rushing to pound their heads against the nearest wall.

Yet, this is what the Air Force must accomplish in its space systems. The Discoverer series of satellites not only must start, stop, and restart the propulsion system on command, but it should change orbit as desired, carry out on-board equipment operations, stabilize the vehicle in attitude with reference to the earth, and then, automatically, and, above all, reliably, prepare its payload for separation from the booster frame. This means carrying out a series of stabilization and attitude control maneuvers, holding a specific attitude and, at an exact moment, igniting another motor to separate a recovery capsule from the satellite. This capsule must be decelerated sufficiently to "break" the orbit and commence return to the earth. Re-entry must be accurate, reliable, and coordinated with a vast recovery system so that the package returned from space may be properly analyzed.

Not only does Discoverer thus provide a means for carrying out extensive research missions in orbit, and for returning biomedical and scientific packages from orbit for more leisurely and effective study here on earth, but it also provides the back-to-earth delivery system for the invaluable camera plates of the Samos satellites.

Discoverer is the Thor-Agena combination. Atlas-Agena, accomplished by placing the Agena atop the Atlas booster, is this system's big brother. Atlas-Agena means earth-orbiting payloads in excess of 3,000 pounds. It means such outstanding reliability and dependability of control that the Atlas-Agena booster system has produced the most precise and accurate orbit ever accomplished, either by the United States or the Soviet Union, in the orbiting of Midas satellites.

NASA has ordered a series of Thor-Agena boosters. Canada's first satellite, launched by the United States, went into its polar orbit atop a Thor-Agena (Discoverer) booster system. The only difference between the Air Force booster and that purchased by NASA was the different name on the side of the vehicle.

The Atlas-Agena B booster system is the propulsion source for
the Midas and Samos satellites. It is also the propulsion source for
sending satellite and deep-space probes to the moon, and to the
planet Venus, by NASA. The only difference between the Air
Force booster and that purchased by NASA was, again, the paint
on the side of the rockets. Indeed, the vehicles were checked out
by Air Force crews, launched from Air Force facilities and, generally, the entire project could have been conducted no matter
what the color of the paint or the extent of the lettering on the side
of the booster vehicles.

It is relevant that the booster system for the Samos, Midas, and
Discoverer satellites originated within the military research and
development structure. Had the Air Force been required from the
very beginning of space activities in this country to await the development of "civilian" boosters, we would not have these vital
surveillance satellites so far along on their development course
today.

In the spring of 1960, the Congress queried Lt. General James
M. Gavin, U.S. Army (Ret.), on the matter of conflict in military
and civilian space activities. General Gavin's views on this subject
are to the point. The General made them clear to the Committee:

> I am of the view, however, that there is but one space pro-
> gram and that one cannot physically separate the nonmilitary
> and the military space activities. In this respect our space
> endeavors parallel closely those in our atomic programs. We
> must have one overall space agency adequately supported,
> from which we will take for military application all the techni-
> cal information that appears to have military usefulness.
> ... Since there is now a "military" program and also a
> "non-military," which is what we like to refer to as the pro-
> gram under NASA, the assumption seems to be that these
> should be continued in this manner. Actually, except for what
> is essentially product improvement, and sufficient research to

make product improvement possible, little progress will be made in the Pentagon without drawing upon the technology, materials and systems and ideas that come out of the NASA program in the future.

A member of the Congressional Committee pursued the subject of surveillance satellites.

> It has been suggested . . . that if the United States had a fleet of Earth satellites equipped with long-range camera equipment with telescopic lenses, and so on . . . it could accurately photograph all of the strategic areas of the U.S.S.R., transmitting that information back to us so that we could know the whereabouts of all their military installations, their launching pads, and so on . . . and in turn, that would reduce the great differential that now exists between Russia and ourselves; that is, a differential in the amount of knowledge that we have about each other. Russia knows everything about us and we know very little about Russia. But by the use of these satellites we will learn all of their secrets; therefore, Russia will not have that trump card, and will be much more susceptible to a disarmament proposal involving inspection, and so on. In this way, peace could be aggressively pursued through space. Would you care to comment on that?
>
> [General Gavin replied:]
>
> If the United Nations were planning well now, it should surely be thinking in terms of contributions made by members to the end that we would have in being a United Nations space patrol, or force, that could keep the Earth under surveillance. What bothers me is that if we fail to appreciate the importance of space and are laggard in our own program, there will come into being a Soviet system that will in fact be a surveillance system and it could be so effective as to deny us use of space if we don't appreciate it and do nothing about it. I think when all is said and done, this is probably the over-riding aspect of the importance of space. It could mean peace on Earth, and lasting peace, if we had the vision

to see what could be done and we did something about it.

[*The question was asked:* Would you say, then, General, that it is most important that Russia not be in a position where she is dominating outer space and this particular area of surveillance satellites?]

Absolutely, absolutely. . . . We would live in misery and number our days in unhappiness for not having had the vision to see this coming. If we ever allowed ourselves to get in that position, it would be impossible.

It must be emphasized that under the present law that established the National Aeronautics and Space Administration, this agency cannot and will not engage in any work of a military nature. Any contributions of the United States through its declared agency for prosecuting the exploration and exploitation of space— to any United Nations system for aiding in spaceborne surveillance over the territory of potential enemies—are thus forbidden. It is for this reason that NASA so often repeats its explanations to the world, and particularly to the Soviet Union, that its Tiros meteorological satellites with their television surveillance cameras lack the ability for any military surveillance system.

The United States has gone to extraordinary lengths to present a picture to the world of a space program dedicated to the cause of peace. It appears strange, then, to have NASA employing the same rocket vehicles and operating from the same installations, in many cases orbiting the same satellite vehicle with only minor variations of interior packaging and at the same time deny the means of contributing a military surveillance capability to the United Nations to aid the cause of peace.

It is our avowed policy not to draw attention to the fact of advanced developments in military space systems; this is, of course, a policy doomed both to ridicule and to failure. We have come to regard space as a thing for manipulation; as a physical entity which we can shape and mold to our convenience. But it is not a substance—it is an environment, and the extension into this environment of the artificial cleavage of our space effort on the ground is monumentally foolish.

Following General Gavin's appearance, Congress requested General Schriever give a more detailed explanation of the space programs of the Air Force. General Schriever's testimony touched off a minor explosion from one of the Committee members. The General pointed out:

> ... in the military we are going to have a relatively large number of satellites for warning purposes, for surveillance purposes, for communications purposes, perhaps later on for satellite defense systems. So our requirement is for relatively large numbers.
>
> I don't see that this will ever be a requirement for civilian exploration of space, because you are going to be building new experimental payloads, you want to get new data, and once you have succeeded in one shot and get this scientific data, you will want to get others, so that you will have fewer shots. You will have changing payloads.
>
> In the military you will attempt to get a payload that is reliable, that can function perhaps for as long as a year in space. We will need to have systems that are simpler to maintain and operate because we have military personnel that will be rotating and we would have to have simplicity in maintenance and operations. NASA will be largely experimental, and research in nature. The X-15 is an example of an aircraft in that category.
>
> I think their space vehicles will be in that sort of a category as well. We need to get low cost per launch. Their emphasis will be to get the highest degree of reliability on a launch. And the cost will be subordinated to that, they want to get performance and reliability for a specific launch. We will be time-oriented; there is an urgency from a defense standpoint. They are time-oriented in a general sense, but we are time-oriented to get there as fast as we possibly can, and also time-oriented when we get the systems—they have to be re-

sponsive. We have to be able to get them off in a hurry when we need them.

I think this degree of urgency requires a bolder approach, a greater calculated risk on the part of the military than on the part of the civilian agency.

And lastly, in the military we have the developer-user relationship. We are talking about a medium, we are not talking about just hardware. We are talking about the ground environment, the people that have to be trained to operate and maintain them, the supply lines, the integration of those systems with other systems in the military. All of these things tend to diverge, I think—the military program from the civilian program. And lastly—I am not interested in going to Venus at this time. Maybe later on I will be. NASA is, today. So they are interested in deep space operation. We are not interested in deep space operation, except from what we gain in terms of scientific and technical knowledge. . . . At some later date we probably will have application.

It was at this point in the hearings that the inevitable finally faced the Committee. Congressman Leonard G. Wolff took on the problem of conflict of operations and responsibilities, emphasizing that—

We have here a fascinating paradox. On the one hand, the President and the Congress have said that we want to pursue space exploration for peaceful purposes with all due speed. On the other hand, we are saying: But we don't want to inhibit our military in any way from getting there. We want them to have the same opportunity in space. What we have tried to do is to capture a propaganda advantage by saying we want to proceed into space peacefully, but yet we are saying, in effect, that we want to modify the law so that it will appear that we can get there with military equipment at the same speed.

. . . I never could see how we could separate the two. I never could buy the idea that you can have peaceful and military exploitation of the same area, and not work together very closely. I noted in your comment here that in the interest of national survival the military must not be inhibited in its activities in exploiting the medium of space and in conducting the research and development in this medium necessary to discharging its basic responsibilities of defense and survival. I agree with this, I agree with this wholeheartedly. But I think this results in the very paradox that I am suggesting. . . .

Why did we go to all the trouble to transfer this program over to NASA, to change our approach to indicate peaceful purposes, when now we seem to say that we don't really mean it at all? Why wouldn't it have been better to have had a strong statement from the military, from the President, and from the Congress to the effect that we want to proceed into space in a peaceful way, but let's not kid ourselves; this is a cruel world we live in, and let's be militarily ready. Let's hope that we can proceed into space using the tools of the military, just as we opened the Panama Canal for peaceful purposes, and yet it has been a tremendous tool for us in time of war.

The contest lay not in the assignment of basic research and scientific investigations to NASA, but in the shadow zones that led to serious problems of interpreting just where NASA authority ended, and military authority, to meet its urgent defense needs, began. The dividing line is not clearly defined, and the shadow zone must be encompassed by the cooperation between the civilian space agency and the military structure.

To date the United States has failed to bridge the gap in a manner assuring the country that its minimum defense needs are to be met. Careful consideration of all the factors involved led to the conviction that the military services, notably the Air Force, were able to define and to meet the needs of the immediate future, in such systems as Samos and Midas. The legal structure established by the Congress, subjected to the intensive and conflicting interpretations of authority, soon shredded the fabric of national military space requirements. The Congress noted clearly that under these conditions: "It has been difficult to fund the investigations that are necessary to find out what space has to offer militarily some years ahead. The military must . . . depend heavily upon NASA for the long look ahead, even though the latter is primarily concerned with peaceful application."

There is the seed of warning for the future in this conclusion, as there is a serious dilution of the military services' capabilities to plan for the situations in which we may become embroiled. If such planning cannot be based on a continuing development of systems and weapons to meet any possible situation this country is going to find itself faced with disastrous consequences.

No one has ever questioned, and no one questions today, the extraordinary capabilities of the personnel of NASA. The scientists, technicians, engineers, and other members of our national space agency take a back seat to no group in the world. It is not the capabilities of NASA about which so much controversy is generated. The question is whether or not the mission of our civilian space agency can meet the needs of the country.

The acquisition of reams of scientific knowledge, the enlarging of our scientific horizons, the sharing of knowledge about the earth and the universe at large—all these are well-defined national goals which must be sustained. But, what if the seeking of these national goals compromises the ability of the United States to meet any national military danger caused by the progress of the Soviet Union in space sciences?

Therein lies the heart of our troubles. The USSR does not distinguish between military and civilian. Their civilian and military structures are joined; their people work together on an extraordinarily close and realistic basis. Russia's space structure is a single entity which they feel is best equipped to meet the national needs of the USSR. They are as anxious and as adept as we in obtaining scientific information. They have achieved a much greater level of competency in assuring that there will be no gaps in their space program which will damage the military position of their country.

In this respect, we are the victims of our own lofty ideals. Scientific acumen is not necessarily consistent with military defense capabilities. In our idealism we appear to have turned a deaf ear to the dangers which may confront us in the future. It is the vast difference between the ability to control space and the exercising of that ability that compromises the philosophical aspirations of the country. We possess today, as we have for many years, the capacity to control the vast air spaces of this planet. But we do not abuse that capacity, and we do not unlimber in arbitrary attacks upon the aircraft of other nations the guns we have carried for years. We are able to sustain our position, from Antarctica to Cuba and Berlin, only because the capacity exists.

If in the future, in space, we encounter situations comparable to those that currently constitute a daily and hazardous existence, and we lack the capability to back up our wishes we will have only one choice. And that is to back down.

Military space requirements are oriented to time; to function within a specific and limited period of time. This is not a requirement of a civilian space agency. It does not have an inherent sense of urgency. And if this is the organization that controls the bulk of the nation's future capabilities in space, then the nation moves into the future without that sense of urgency.

That can be fatal.

CHAPTER 10.

TO DEFEND THIS NATION

IT is not readily apparent that major national decisions, once committed to organizations and policies, play a major role in the future of the United States. A case in point is the old NACA—the National Advisory Committee for Aeronautics. In 1915, as this country struggled to emerge from the critical weaknesses that made us a tenth-rate power among the air nations of the world, the Congress established the NACA. It was a unique organization. It did not carry out the development of aircraft, and yet it played a qualitative role in producing what finally became many of the leading aircraft of the world.

The military services turned to the NACA to meet their most pressing problems in aeronautical design and science. The airlines did the same. Private companies, large and small, flocked to NACA in their quest for aid and assistance in improving existing designs, or in accomplishing breakthroughs into new levels of achievement in design and performance.

If the Air Force produced a new experimental fighter airplane, for example, it would run that machine through extensive testing and modification. When the tests were complete, the airplane would then be sent to NACA and NACA scientists were turned loose on the machine.

The NACA scientists subjected the new airplane to batteries of exhausting tests. They would place both the airplane and models of it into a variety of wind tunnels. They would leave nothing untouched and no area free from scrutiny. When the airplane was returned to the Air Force, it would often look almost the same as when it had left. But not quite. There would be minor differences; the movement of the exhaust plumbing, a change in position and design of a radio mast, a minor added curve in an air scoop, a different type of door for the landing gear, a subtle shift in the curvature of a plastic canopy.

Whatever the visible extent of the changes, the performance changes often were astonishing. One single-engine fighter, accepted for production as a first-line weapon, went through the NACA grinder. When the airplane emerged from NACA, its changes were minor and subtle. But they were extremely significant. Without adding any power to the fighter, the NACA scientists increased its speed by more than fifty miles per hour. The airplane gained a free dividend of a greater two hundred mile range. It took off faster, and landed in shorter distances. It climbed faster and higher than before. It became, in other words, a superior weapon.

In every respect NACA received the unanimous and enthusiastic support of the military services and of the aviation community at large. NACA's facilities often stood on military installations, side by side with the machines of war. Its laboratories and testing sites spread across the entire United States. It is considered to be perhaps the most successful scientific and engineering endeavor by the United States. It proved a major factor in the ascendancy of American aeronautical science to a position of world leadership.

In 1958, the new National Aeronautics and Space Administration (NASA) absorbed the old NACA. All the facilities, the personnel, and the vast experience accumulated by NACA thus established a solid, scientific foundation for the new space agency. The only sounds of opposition to this move came from those individuals and groups who felt that the country might lose the unique

characteristics of the NACA, swallowed within the much larger
NASA organization. It appears inevitable that in the need to meet
the demands of space exploration, NACA would have to serve in
its new role of foundation builder.

With this understanding of the role of NACA, it becomes easier
to understand the major differences between the former agency that
functioned in advisory capacity and NASA. The space agency is
not an advisory organization. It is a huge structure of government that decides and dictates policies, that represents the United
States as the primary organization to fulfill space exploration for
this country.

As such, NASA dictates rigid policies. It bestows contracts involving billions of dollars and has a direct working staff of several tens
of thousands of people. It already operates dozens of major installations and facilities throughout the United States, and it is building many, many more. NASA exerts a profound and, often, an
overwhelming influence upon the well-being of hundreds of communities throughout the country. In more than one instance, a
NASA contract has meant the difference between economic pros-
perity and economic anemia for a community.

NASA functions as one of the most critical elements of the position we will maintain in the future. Inherent in the NASA structure,
however, are several basic flaws. For one, this new organization
did not come into being in response to a well-established national
need. It blossomed out of a severe defeat at the hands of the
Russians. In its formative steps it suffered from the earnest, ideal-
istic desire of its founders to function as an organization without
the taint of military overtones. With commendable eagerness the
founders of NASA sought to pave the way to a future resplendent
with peaceful uses of space. In earnest pursuit of this goal, they
inevitably tended to shut their eyes to the realities of the world in
which we live.

NASA rests on this troubled foundation. Were this a world in which nations did not mistrust one another and have the means to exercise that lack of trust in devastating, thermonuclear fashion, it would be difficult to conceive of an organization better suited to our national aspirations than NASA.

For the first half-dozen years of the age of space, it has been possible to avoid the unpleasant fact that one day we must run headlong into the conflict created by the power in NASA's hands. Congress proclaimed in 1958 that NASA shall be responsible for our entire civilian space program. This was also representative of the opinion and willing cooperation of the military and industrial organizations of this land.

This system worked before, and worked superbly in the form of NACA. Many people wish fervently that the same rapport can again be established, that NASA will function as did NACA. This, however, is impossible. NACA constituted an advisory group —NASA formulates, orders, and conducts its own operations. In order to fulfill its responsibilities as defined by the Congress, NASA must exercise authority. This is not only within its province; it is its assigned function. Thus there must come a clash—and one with overtones reverberating not only throughout the nation, but across an international framework as well.

The clash is easily defined. The military services are also bound to fulfill a mission as specified by the Congress. That mission is to defend this nation against any danger that is presently known or that may be foretold under any and all circumstances.

In order to do so, the men who run the military structure, and who are the most capable in defining its needs and anticipating its future problems, must be able to plan for that future. Such planning not only involves but demands the foresight that allows us to meet future technological requirements.

The situation may be compared to historical problems. The United States emerged victorious from World War II as the most powerful wielder of airpower in the world. We met—and wrecked

—the best of the opposition. We did so with piston-engine airplanes that pounded through the skies behind propellers that
thrashed noisily and with gross inefficiency.

Germany was the only nation that fought her air war with a
substantial quantity of jet aircraft. Her jets streaked through the
skies at speeds well over five hundred miles per hour and her
swallow-shaped rocket interceptors flashed against our bombers
at more than six hundred miles per hour.

Germany lost that air war. Engineers who studied the jet engines of those days concluded, and rightfully so, that the piston
engine was more efficient, and more reliable. The jets consumed
staggering quantities of fuel and suffered from limited range. The
engineers carried their conclusions further; the jets, they said,
were interesting, and would be useful in meeting certain aspects of
air missions. But the present and the future belonged to the airplane with a propeller.

Today there is not a single combat airplane in the Air Force
with a propeller. Not one of the fighters in production for the military services is less than supersonic in level flight. Only because a
long-range program was instituted in this new science of aero-
dynamics could we achieve this present status without falling mor-
tally behind the USSR which, being realistic, has pursued with
much more diligence the goal of an airpower second to none.

In the process of moving into the jet age, the military services
worked closely both with industry and with NACA. The Air Force
and the Navy did not design or produce their own jet engines.
They left this task, as they had done before, to the scientists and
engineers of the aviation industry. And in an outstanding triangle
of cooperation, the military, industry and NACA worked together
toward a single goal.

We built the jets we needed. From those military jet engines, the
industry produced the finest and most reliable commercial jet engines in the world.

Under the present system of national authority and priorities, the Air Force no longer may press the research and development programs it needs to assure a continuing growth and development of weapons systems and, most of all, of weapons systems technology. One cannot do these things overnight. The lead time, from inception of design to availability of hardware on an operational basis, will extend from a minimum of about six to an average of eight years.

This lesson came home to us painfully in the opening shots of the space competition. Over and over again people cried for a crash program to overcome the Soviet lead in boosters. But the magic formula of crash priority and dollars failed to erase our weakness in rocket power. Lead time was the key and we had forfeited lead time to the USSR. Had there not been the old Navaho program based on the foundation of large rocket engine technology, we would still be much farther behind the Russians than we are today.

And we are still, at the beginning of 1963, far behind in boosters.

1) The heaviest payload sent into orbit by the United States to date is of approximately the same weight as the third Russian satellite, launched in May, 1958.

2) The heaviest payload sent by the United States on trajectory to the moon is less than the weight of the payloads sent to the moon by the Russians in 1959.

3) In November, 1962, the United States could send a payload to the planet Mars weighing no more than 200 pounds. For this reason, a Mars probe scheduled for that time was canceled. The Soviet Union fired a Mars probe with a payload of 2,000 pounds—ten times heavier than our best efforts could produce.

4) The heaviest American payload in earth orbit is about 3,500 pounds. In February, 1961, the Russians orbited several payloads each more than 14,000 pounds in weight, and in 1962 the USSR

was regularly orbiting satellite payloads of approximately 17,000 pounds or more.

These facts should remind us of our present position in space. It is too easy to forget these uncomfortable matters. And the key to all this is booster power. Why didn't we have a crash program? Again it is lead time. As one unhappy scientist has said, "We have the best hospitals and the best obstetricians, but it still takes nine months."

This brings us to a problem which the Air Force considers acute and becoming more critical with every passing month. The Air Force no longer is able to press a development program under its own decision no matter how vital that program may be to the future security of the United States. The decision is not in the hands of the Air Force now, and has not been for several years. The decision rests in the top echelons of the Department of Defense.

This seems sensible, for the people in the Department of Defense (DOD) represent the military, and they will decide what the Air Force or any other military organization shall or shall not do.

But the officials who make the decisions of the Department of Defense are not military personnel. They are, like the top officials of NASA, civilians. The system of military control in the United States is, specifically, civilian control of the military organizations. It is not to this system that so many objections have been raised. It is to the fact that the DOD personnel, the so-called Pentagon whiz-kids, are blinded by the niceties of technological development.

Apparently these men cannot see imperative long-range military requirements for the slide rules that surround them. They want answers of black-and-white when questioning military planners on requests and proposals for long-range military space systems developments. It is nice to have everything in black and white, but it doesn't work out very well in practice.

On January 11, 1961, President-elect Kennedy released the report of the Ad Hoc Committee on Space. This item was in the report.

> Each of the military Services has begun to create its own independent space program. This presents the problem of overlapping programs and duplication of the work of NASA. If the responsibility of all military space developments were to be assigned to one agency or military Service within the Department of Defense, the Secretary of Defense would then be able to maintain control of the scope and direction of the program and the Space Council would have the responsibility for settling conflicts of interest between NASA and the Department of Defense.

The recommendations implicit in this statement went into effect shortly thereafter and Secretary of Defense Robert McNamara assigned "space development programs and projects to the Department of the Air Force, except under unusual circumstances."

The Department of Defense publicly hailed this move as a significant step in the consolidation of military space development activities, noting that it would prevent undue duplication of effort. Many an eyebrow went up over this claim to increased efficiency because, as Deputy Defense Secretary Roswell L. Gilpatric admitted, the "Air Force was already responsible for over 90 percent of the total defense effort in space development activities, either by direct assignment or in support of other programs."

The civilian heads of the Department of Defense carried the ultimate authority for assigning roles and missions—and what these civilian authorities believed to be adequate for military space needs was often distressingly far removed from the views held by the military planners themselves.

The DOD is adamant on proof of mission needs in space. Just as the old General Staff bitterly fought the program of building four-engine bombers, repetitiously grinding out the question of "whom are we going to bomb, since no one would ever dare attack us across the ocean?", so the present staff functions on the basis of a show-me policy.

In essence, the DOD staff insists upon a clearly demonstrated need for any Air Force research program. And the need has to be justified on the basis of how the program will operate in the shortest possible time.

It is flatly impossible to give such clear-cut lines to many military space weapons. Samos and Midas are obvious. There are other programs well under development; one was known as Saint. It involved a satellite with capabilities and equipment demonstrated by the Discoverer program. Saint was to be a satellite interceptor. It would go into an orbit to match that of a Russian satellite of which we have no identification. Then, through an elaborate electronic system, and an amazing propulsion system flexibility, Saint would close the distance between itself and its "target"—changing orbit and velocity until it was close enough to the other satellite for Saint's cameras and other instruments to examine the unknown orbiter in great detail.

The Air Force wanted to build into Saint not only an interception and study capability, but also a destructive capability. Then if such close and careful study of the other satellite determined that it posed a threat, it would be Saint's mission to destroy the satellite.

But there is a limit, after all, to what automatic systems can do. And the best automatic system cannot hope to match the superb engineering combination of the man-machine system.

After years of study, Saint in late 1962 went on the scrap heap. It was to be the forerunner of a manned satellite interceptor. But DOD has now ruled that the high costs of Saint forced this effort's disposal, and has sounded the death-knell of the manned Saint vehicle. The manned space combat capability which the Air Force felt was vital in Saint is now only a memory.

The problem in this situation is that the Department of Defense had ruled that the Air Force cannot justify a manned space program. Until recently this ruling was absolute, and the breach only came in the form of a bitterly fought-for and long-awaited green light on the Dyna-Soar program. Dyna-Soar is a manned spaceship, making maximum use of the tremendous flexibility of a man's capacity for decision-making and control of a vehicle. It is interesting to note that the Air Force originally failed to gain more than grudging, limited financial support and official authorization for this basic building block of future manned combat spaceship systems. Only after the program was renamed X-20, "an experimental program to explore the problems of re-entry from orbit in a vehicle of high aerodynamic maneuverability," did the go-ahead signal appear.

The Air Force considers programs such as Dyna-Soar and the manned Saint as indispensable to the long-term defense of the United States. But it may not institute such research activities on its own, and it must abide by the decisions handed down from the desk-strata of the DOD.

These decisions are driving many a military and industrial engineer to distraction. After years of intensive development, Saint felt the DOD guillotine. The *only* manned space program remaining in the Air Force was the critical X-20 Dyna-Soar. Extensive development contracts and hundreds of subcontracts were let. Plans for years of development and testing were established.

At the present moment, DOD is once again casting a baleful eye over the entire X-20 program. The murmur swells to a disconcerting roar that DOD regards the X-20 as too costly, as too remote in mission concept, as beyond the province of the Air Force as a justifiable program. Where is the specific military mission of the X-20 Dyna-Soar? DOD insists upon this answer, but at this moment there can be none.

No Air Force officer would wager so much as a dime on the chances of the X-20 Dyna-Soar to remain the major program it is now scheduled to be. The word in the Pentagon is that the X-20 will either suffer a major cutback in funds and in priority—or that it may be canceled altogether.

This would leave the military establishment of our nation without *any* manned space flight program. The possibility delights the Soviets.

The military services are not entirely crippled by these restrictions on research. Limited flexibility is allowed in that the various components of the Department of Defense may conduct "preliminary research to develop ways of using space technology to perform its assigned function." But such preliminary research does not always fit future needs and weapons, since DOD maintains a rigid clamp on any expenditures. In addition, DOD has warned the Services that: "No military department or other Defense agency is authorized to go beyond the defined scope of preliminary research unless and until the program or project has received the express approval of either the Secretary or the Deputy Secretary."

To obtain such approval means going through a labyrinth of authorizations and justifications over which there looms the specter of trying to prove the immediate need and use of the end product of such research as a weapon or weapon-support system. Anyone familiar with the tortured channels of such military justification can well appreciate the problems involved, all compounded by the situation in which the "show me" requirement is often impossible to meet.

Especially significant is this explanation by Assistant Secretary Gilpatric:

> It should be noted that the Department of the Air Force does not select what projects are to be developed. In this respect, the Department of the Air Force is only another proponent of equal status with the other Services and there is no different situation than the Army or the Navy. It must come forward and justify projects which it wants with just as much support and validity as the other agencies do theirs.

Thus the burden for a long-range, sustained space program falls directly on the ability to establish beyond any doubt that the program will produce a weapon that is needed now, or in the immediate future. During the period when the military services of this country carried out virtually all space research (the only exception being Vanguard, which itself emerged from the Naval Research Laboratory), this same policy proved to be nearly disastrous to the United States. Today, NASA calls special attention to its enormous Saturn I booster rocket. Saturn is a giant. It weighs more than a million pounds at launch, and it leaves the earth with all the howling fury that represents one and a half million pounds' thrust—a power equal to a cluster of twenty rockets of the type that sent Alan Shepard into space.

Saturn I is one of our great hopes for getting back into the booster race. NASA is repetitious on the fact that our civilian space agency, through the tremendous energy of this rocket, will by 1965 be sending into space payloads nearly seven times heavier than our Mercury spacecraft. But Saturn is not a civilian booster. It is a military rocket, planned to place massive satellites in orbit at 22,300 miles beyond the earth. Its name of Saturn is a replacement for its original title, Juno V.

In 1959, Saturn, or Juno V, was a project of the United States Army. The original satellite program planned for the giant booster was downgraded. There was absolutely no question but that this country would have a growing and critical need for this huge rocket. But in 1959, the military agencies of the United States could not justify the Saturn program on the basis of a weapon or weapon system under accelerated development. And in 1959, two years after Sputnik, the Department of Defense decided to cancel the entire Saturn program.

Roy W. Johnson, Director of the Advanced Research Projects Agency, was advised by Dr. Herbert York, Director of Defense Research and Engineering, Department of Defense, that he had decided to cancel the Saturn. Mr. Johnson has testified under oath before the Congress that he was informed of this decision in August of 1959.

One can imagine the bitter fight of the military to retain this program. In 1959, when the Russians were rifling their massive payloads to the moon with a precision which this country has yet to achieve, we ordered the end of the most powerful rocket in the United States.

It could not be "justified." There was no weapon we were to place atop this booster. Funds could not be authorized on the basis of a long-range program. Therefore the program had to be wiped out.

At the last moment, the Department of Defense made an eleventh-hour decision to transfer the Saturn to NASA.

The same situation which existed in 1959 in the face of a mounting Russian storm into space and which could cancel this crucial program has not changed at all. This is why our military officials are more than concerned. If the pattern is not changed, the same extraordinary decisions can be made, again and again, until the Russians finally achieve a lead in space technology so substantial that the term "the peaceful uses of space" will become a mockery.

CHAPTER **11.**

A CALL TO ARMS

NO one example can serve better than the case history of the great Saturn booster to emphasize the weakness in the present system of providing us with the military strength we may one day need in space. The weakness is of course a human one. There is a general tendency in attempting to forecast the future to be optimistic about what can be achieved within a period of several years but to be far too cautious about the events which will transpire within two or three decades.

We tend to base our thinking on hardware terms, rather than upon concepts. We must disabuse ourselves of the outmoded concept that unless we can tie a ribbon about a weapons system it is wasteful to expend money on long-term military research. This policy is not only financially wasteful, it is militarily dangerous. Far more important, long-range military research provides the nation with a sound base of technological capabilities.

Why do we use the term *aerospace?* The question serves to illuminate the sharp divergence between our civilian space agency and the military. NASA finds in its manned spacecraft vehicles that its needs are met by a blunt-edged shape, familiar to us in the form of the Mercury capsule. NASA has little if any need at this time to push toward a vehicle requiring directional control and pilot capability in its return from space to the earth. The briefest, crudest method of return is acceptable. And this represents crashing back into the atmosphere, an explosively fiery descent, like a huge artificial meteor, and then a swaying and drifting drop beneath billowing parachutes.

This meets the needs of NASA and the programs for manned space flight known as Mercury (one man), Gemini (two men), and Apollo (three men). It meets only temporarily, and partially, the needs of the Air Force, which holds to the line that there does not exist an arbitrary or artificial division between the upper atmosphere and space.

Can anyone doubt that the Soviet Union is not studying every possible military advantage to be obtained from operations in the aerospace environment? It is difficult to consider even briefly that the Russians have blinded themselves to the military advantages in any area or environment. Neither can one doubt that in their search, they will waste any time in pursuing to the maximum extent, the means of developing the vehicles, systems, and weapons that will enable them to gain any level of military superiority. So it is all the more incredible that at this late stage of the competition for space the United States does not have a military, manned space program.

Under the DOD operation the United States Air Force cannot demonstrate conclusively, beyond any question, to the Department of Defense that it needs, now, imperatively, a complete manned combat system for space operations.

What drives Air Force officials to schizophrenia is that they have to admit that we do not need this system now, but that certainly the need will be imperative before the decade is out. However, without the justification for the immediate need, the Air Force cannot move ahead with its own manned space program. It must fight its way in through the back door to space.

A manned military space system demands a long and costly

development cycle. If it is stretched out over a period of years it can be integrated into co-existing research programs, such as Discoverer, and the cost is drastically reduced.

This country is in dire need of advanced research operations in the bioastronautic sciences of space flight. We are disastrously far behind the Soviet Union in this field and even were we able to match the Russians, we would still find it necessary to carry out experiments with animals in space that cannot be duplicated with men.

Years back the Air Force bioastronautics program for manned space flight began to move into high gear. The rockets were not yet ready, but they were under accelerated tests as ballistic missiles. Planning for the day when these vehicles would become available for use, as they did in the spectacularly successful Discoverer program, the Air Force organized and assembled a superb collection of facilities for this research.

At Holloman Air Force Base in New Mexico, a chimpanzee colony of several hundred animals was begun. Scientists ran extensive experiments with the chimps. Patterns of behavior began to show which contributed much useful knowledge when the chimpanzees Ham and Enos were sent into space by NASA.

The Air Force had planned to send chimpanzees into space within special capsules that would be boosted by the Discoverer satellite series. The Thor-Agena rockets would place the chimpanzees into varying types of orbits and subject them (other test animals were also included in the program) to the full spectrum of weightlessness, acceleration and deceleration, orbital tumbling and gyration, exposure to cosmic radiation, and the radiation belts of the earth.

Since then the Air Force has quietly bemoaned the fate of the program as it was shot down by the "show me" policy of the DOD. It is a poorly kept secret in Washington that NASA officials made known to the Department of Defense their displeasure at the Air Force bioastronautics-chimpanzee program. DOD officials were

reminded that the Air Force did not have a manned space program. Without such an effort as authorized by DOD, there did
not exist any justifiable need to research the bioastronautics field
in space flight and the Air Force was told to cancel the program.

And so for the last few years, that great chimpanzee colony has
been wasted, the biocapsules for the animals have collected dust on
the shelves, and the great need for extensive information in the bioastronautics field, in which we trail the Soviet Union by several
years, has gone begging and unanswered. We are and have been
and will be for some time paying the penalty for this incredible
stupidity.

NASA scientists now are looking forward to extensive experiments on a long-term basis with chimpanzees in orbit about the
earth. They plan to use several of the Mercury capsules that will
be left over from that program—to be canceled as soon as the
new two-man Gemini program begins in 1964. It is not possible
to send a man into space with a probe imbedded within his brain.
This is one of many experiments NASA scientists aver they must
conduct in order that we may plan for sustained flights of men in
space or on duty aboard manned stations orbiting the earth.

The chimpanzees will, of course, be obtained from the Air
Force animal colony at Holloman. And in either 1963 or 1964,
NASA will begin its new bioastronautics research effort, starting
a program the Air Force began years ago, and then was forced to
cancel, because a military manned space program did not exist.

Weapons costs in our day and age are staggering. The ICBM
program will cost this country more than five times as much as
the wartime crash development of the atomic bomb. And that
single effort, the Manhattan Project, cost more than two billion
dollars.

Thus it is necessary to be extremely selective in deciding upon
new weapons. Strategic weapons are not simply weapons; they
are complete systems. And the entity formed by a weapons system consists not only of the operational product, but the training

facilities, logistics, communications, spares, replacements and other support elements.

Selectivity is the keynote to the proper planning of these extraordinarily costly items. Thus some freedom of selection within the framework of planning is necessary, and the freedom of selection can be applied sensibly only by those closest to the subject. It cannot be decided on a policy basis by people who lack either the experience in hard military affairs or the sense of urgency that such planning must have.

The DOD "show me" policy creates a situation in which we delay to a critical point until (1) there is no argument that the system has an imperative and crucial need, and (2) as a result of this imbalance there is a subsequent situation in which demonstrations of the technical feasibility of the system are so long delayed that obsolescence, like arthritis, sets in before the weapons system may be put in use.

The expression "basic building blocks" has worked its way into planning considerations for future weapons systems; and the concept, valid in its premise but void in its execution under present policies, is to conduct both fundamental and applied research in order that technological-military capabilities progress on a general front. This policy, if it had DOD support rather than DOD lip-service, would enable our military agencies to progress in the shortest possible time from concept to reality. The process, of course, entails a broad spectrum of research even when the specific weapons system is not in sight.

Had this policy been followed, the Air Force would have been permitted to move ahead rapidly in its bioastronautics program using chimpanzees for advanced biomedical research. It should be noted that in this effort the rocket booster vehicles already were in existence. The launching sites and tracking facilities were in operation. The chimpanzee training program was well established. The recovery vehicles for re-entry were proven hardware items. Funds, which were extremely low in comparison to other programs, had already been provided. And there was no question that we would have to get this data from an animal research program in orbit in the near future. But the "building-block concept," ruled DOD, did not allow for the program.

The decision on this matter is hardly different from the orders issued in Washington in 1956 that forbade the Army to send a satellite, with a rocket already at Cape Canaveral, into orbit.

The point has been raised in the past, and it is being raised with increasing frequency at present, that the Air Force should stay out of basic research. Were this premise ever to be executed as policy, the blow to the United States would be devastating. With the presently held attitude of the "civilian only—military keep out" programs, there has been a babble that only civilian-run scientific organizations should be responsible for basic research.

The scientific studies of the water vapor content of the stratosphere are regarded by most as a purely scientific research effort, and complaints have been registered to the effect that Air Force research in this area is a clear overstepping of the boundaries of this service. These allegations are ridiculous, for such geophysical studies are vital to the Air Force so it may conduct its combat and surveillance missions.

The Midas program, which will cost several billion dollars in its long-term and final form, employs infrared systems that detect the flight of ballistic missiles above the troposphere. In order that such detection may be evaluated with the great accuracy that the Midas warning system requires, it is absolutely necessary to know the water vapor content of the stratosphere, and its effect upon infrared measurements. Civilian scientists had never attempted such measurements to any extent and the Air Force suffered a paucity of data. Thus the urgent requirement for a program of geophysical measurements in this area.

Fundamental research within the Air Force is carried out extensively in the broad areas of propulsion, materials, electronics, geophysics, biosciences, and aeromechanics. And in these areas it is impossible to tell beforehand just what vital military benefits will accrue. But the past record of substantial technological breakthroughs is so extensive that the thought of restricting this research is frightening.

It is obvious that basic research serves as the midwife to a healthy military science technology. Defining basic research is as difficult as trying to find the beginning and the end of a wrestler's neck, but an acceptable explanation is that basic research is that type of research which is directed toward the increase of knowledge.

This is a subject so diverse and so vast that it is almost impossible to deal with. Yet extraordinary work is performed in the Air Force, the Navy, and the Army in the areas of both basic and applied research. The range of definite and vital contributions to the body of scientific and technological knowledge is staggering and still research is conducted not only for the "advancement of science," but also to anticipate areas in which these developments vitally affect the security of the nation.

The Air Force's need for knowledge to carry out its mission of operations within or beyond the atmospheric ocean of the planet can hardly be arbitrarily defined. Solar storms were long held to lie entirely beyond the province of Air Force concerns—yet it is necessary to understand radiation levels in space and their effects not only upon the atmospheric mantle of earth, but also on objects sent into space. The Soviet Union has conducted the most extensive research activities in this area of any nation. This is essential for the protection of the men sent into space, and even more so for the protection of the crews the Russians intend to keep in space for weeks at a time.

Sunspots and solar electrical storms greatly and sometimes disastrously affect the communications systems and facilities of our military services. Can there be a dispute over the need for the most efficient, effective and reliable communications across the planet so that this country might conduct its military operations? It is as vital to the assurance of the security of this nation as is the design of a new wing or automatic cannon. Yet, this is "pure research."

The civilian space programs we enjoy today originated with the military need of assuring operations no matter what the external environment. The Transit navigation satellite program stems from the urgent requirement for accurate navigation under any weather conditions, anywhere on this earth—and Transit came into being as a military requirement. So did our communications satellites, and many of our radiation monitoring satellites, and those "basic and pure research" vehicles which we fling into the celestial vaults about our planet.

Few programs have enjoyed as much publicity as our meteorological satellite, best known in the form of Tiros. It is presumptuous to regard this program as one born of our civilian space effort, for the weather satellites were spawned by the critical need of our Air Force and Navy to meet operational requirements anywhere in the world and during any type of weather. After they emerged from their original security cloak as a military program, our meteorological satellites were touted as the product of this nation's advanced thinking in carrying out space efforts for the enrichment of man's knowledge. It should be added that before the orbiting of Sputnik meteorological satellites enjoyed little more scientific support than the presentation of technical papers at conferences and meetings.

So the Air Force, as the military agency responsible for the hard core and the bulk of this nation's military space developments, must sustain its endless cycle of research, development, refinement and testing. It would seem less than appropriate for Air Force scientists to engage in detailed studies of beetles. Yet one of the experiments with beetles led directly to the development of the most accurate groundspeed indicator for aircraft yet devised. In this particular experiment, the beetle was suspended rigidly in the center of a rotating drum. The walls of the drum were painted with alternating black and white panels. As the drum revolved, the beetle's eyes responded to the brightness of the white panels.

Scientists discovered that the beetle's eyes performed a continuous autocorrelation of a random pattern of light. The beetle's responses were measured by the movement of a rounded object that it clutched with its feet and turned in response to the stimulus from the patterns of light. The movement of the object indicated the direction of movement the beetle would have taken if it had been free. When this autocorrelation was worked out mathematically, it became apparent that an analogous mechanical system could be devised.

Each biological unit involved in the perception of motion was translated into an electronic counterpart. Thus photoelectric cells placed at the front and rear of an airplane were substituted for the beetle's ommatidia. Appropriate integrators and other electronic units completed this highly accurate groundspeed indicator. The sensory cells or receivers on the aircraft registered passage over the same point on the earth and, using a light source, measured the length of time between the passage of the first and second sensors over the point on the ground, giving the groundspeed. As "basic research," the investigation of the reaction of beetles to light stimulation could hardly be justified in terms of weapons systems.

CHAPTER 12.

ROLES AND MISSIONS

IT is hazardous to prepare a list of final accomplishments of the USSR in space in order to establish a level of comparison with our own capabilities and deficiencies. Events in this new age move so swiftly and with such meaning that by the time anything on this subject reaches print, vast changes have taken place. Soviet capabilities in space are both formidable and frightening. It is unfortunate that the American public is so poorly informed of these capabilities compared with ours—unfortunate because in recent times there has come to exist a rosy glow about what we can do in terms of space shots and operations. The truth of the matter is that we are really not doing so well at all.

In a world without competition in space exploration, and without knowing any better, most of our body scientific, and the official and general public as well, were willing to accept our national standards in the form of Vanguard. This rocket, an engineering triumph but a puny vehicle for space exploration, now is looked upon as the frailest of space vessels when compared to the behemoths in orbit today.

We have little choice but to judge ourselves on the basis of Russian accomplishments—for the simple reason that this is the manner of judgment of the entire world. And while the American public is often spoon-fed meaningless comparisons, deprecations, and grandiose claims, there can be no evasion of the hard fact that the Soviet Union has demonstrated an extraordinary capacity for skillful accomplishments in space.

It is important to note that the Congress has evinced a growing concern through the years in respect to the steady deterioration in the power of the United States to stand against increasing Soviet power. This seems incongruous and even downright impossible, in view of our overwhelming strategic bomber fleet, our rapidly increasing number of missiles on combat-alert status, and the evidence of great national strength exhibited during the Cuban crisis late in 1962. But it is not in the medium of airpower that the great decisions of the future may be reached.

> . . . the Soviet Union in the last several years has demonstrated a great skill in coordinating its progress in missilery, its success in space missions, and its foreign policy and world image. Shots seem to have been timed to maximize the effects of visits of Soviet leaders and to punctuate Soviet statements and positions in international negotiations. This is not to equate their space activities with hollow propaganda. Empty claims do not have a positive effect for long. Nor is there any firm evidence that it has been possible for political policy-makers to call their shots at times inconsistent with good scientific and technical needs. The conclusion is rather that the many elements of scientific, technical, military, political, and psychological policy are all weighed, and tests which make a full contribution to such a combined strategy are carried out and supported with appropriate publicity.*

Ever since the beginning of the exploration of space, the Russians have been up and running with all their national strength. Our own progress represents considerably less effort, a lower-keyed cognizance of future risks and dangers, and an alarmingly slow pace of recognizing the pitfalls awaiting our failure to match or exceed the Russians in space advances.

* "Space, Missiles, and the Nation," Report of the House Committee on Science and Astronautics, May 1960.

In the evaluations of the Congress on the subject of our dangerous weaknesses in military space capabilities, we are provided with
a rare insight into the problem. The fear is that if the competition
becomes any more one-sided than it is today we may awake one
day to find ourselves staring at a military dilemma of disastrous
consequences. The warning is provided in the following excerpts
from a Congressional Report prepared some three and a half
years after the orbiting of the first two Russian satellites in 1957.*
Especially to be noted is the somber tone of this document:

> Currently, the United States finds itself in the position of
> competing with the Soviet Union in space activities. Although
> this competition may not be acknowledged, the psychological
> effect of its outcome on the peoples of all nations may tip
> the world balance of power in favor of the winner. It is also
> conceivable that *eventual military uses of space may be of such
> magnitude as to transcend existing military concepts* [em-
> phasis added].
>
> ... There may have been a tendency in some quarters to
> minimize the significance of Soviet attainments. The United
> States has the problems of counteracting any military threat
> imposed and, at the same time, of preserving the belief of
> the free world in its ultimate technological victory. This coun-
> try will be forced to spend more and more of its resources
> in detecting and tracking Soviet satellites either announced or
> designed for surveillance of the United States. ...
>
> ... there must be a clear statement of national intent in the
> exploitation of space. It should contain an indication of the
> progress desired in relation to that of our potential enemies.
> A logical national objective might be: *To maintain world
> leadership in the peaceful exploitation of space and astronauti-
> cal sciences and to insure that military applications in the
> area are energetically prosecuted in the interest of national
> security.*

* Hearings before the Committee on Science and Astronautics, U.S. House
of Representatives, May 1961, Report No. 10.

. . . It is not difficult to appreciate the military advantages of Earth-orbiting satellites for communication, reconnaissance, meteorological, and navigation purposes. . . . As presently organized and staffed, it is not clear that NASA is in a position to direct its attention to military potentials of space with the same thought and concern given the extension of our scientific knowledge. NASA is engaged in a space program primarily directed to peaceful applications. . . . With the transfer of many of the DOD space-oriented resources to NASA, the onus of new accomplishments that may ultimately be applicable to military systems may shift to the latter agency. In the present state of technology, it is difficult to tell what is peaceful and what is a military application.

. . . *NASA is directed to tell the military if it finds information of military value, but the determination is not necessarily made with military counsel.* . . . there is no requirement that the NASA program contribute extensively to the future military capability needed to enhance the national security.

Mr. Roy W. Johnson, civilian director of the Advanced Research Projects Agency, has bluntly stated on more than one occasion his concern for the military needs of the United States. Rather than sit back and echo the policies of the Department of Defense, Mr. Johnson has instead pursued vigorously the theme that his responsibilities dictate that he present the facts and needs of the nation as he sees them. Thus Mr. Johnson's candor illuminates brilliantly the committee-room walls which have echoed dully to evasive statements and, it must be noted, earns Mr. Johnson not the plaudits of his associates and superiors, but rather their disfavor.

For Roy Johnson is bitterly opposed to a divergence of national effort in our space program, and he despairs of the artificial foundation upon which our space policy rests. He sees this insecure structure as: ". . . a widespread almost emotional movement to declare space, like Antarctica, a peaceful place, and this is as hopeless of being effective as declaring ground, air, or water exclusively peaceful."

And then Mr. Johnson—in the words of the Congress—"fired both barrels." He attacked the structure that permitted conflict to interfere with the development of military space systems as "only giving lip service" to the vital needs of the national defense. He ripped into the officials who tried to cancel the great Saturn booster rocket and added:

> . . . to say the Saturn has no military utility, no military usefulness . . . that is just the shortest sighted thinking, and I get concerned that we have that kind of thinking, because it definitely indicates that we are not looking down the road any ten or fifteen years.
>
> . . . military people have got to be concerned with the defense of our country. You can't turn this over to civilians. I feel that we have got to find some way to make the Joint Chiefs of Staff work. I believe the Joint Chiefs have got to do this job, and think it through, and we have got to give them the confidence and the money to back them up.
>
> . . . This idea that there is no purpose for a man in space, was enunciated, I think, as a part of the President's primer that there is no reason to have a man in space [for military missions]. I have disagreed with that statement, violently disagreed with that statement. Yet that statement is constantly being made. There again, eminent scientists continue to talk this way, and I am greatly concerned why they must insist on this. What is wrong with a man in uniform being in space? What is wrong with him being on the land, in the air, and water?
>
> . . . we are thinking from the wrong posture. I am all for scientific space exploration. I don't know how much I am willing to spend on it as a taxpayer; I am talking about pure science. I think that ought to be a collateral thing rather than the principal thing.

I think that we now know that space offers a new threat to

our national security. I think we should turn this job over with all the authority to the people who are responsible for our security. Then I think if we want to have expeditions for scientific work that have no military implications, let's have them in a neat little niche over here someplace and fund it as we fund anything scientific, but first we must make the military people understand that they have this primary responsibility.

Several years later the situation remained basically unchanged. The primary responsibility did not lie in the hands of military leaders. It did not lie within the province of NASA. And NASA, in fact, was forbidden even to delve into this area. The face presented to the world must be kept shining and pure.

The flight of cosmonaut Gherman S. Titov in Vostok II in August of 1961 sent tremors of dismay and uncertainty shivering through the space structure of the country. Nearly four years had passed since the first Russian satellite and instead of our closing the gap, it appeared that the Russians were still pulling away.

When Titov completed his seventeen orbits of the earth in a massive, five-ton spaceship some twelve feet wide and twenty-two feet long, the United States had still not placed a single man in orbit within our cramped, one-and-a-half-ton satellite. And then, Glenn and Carpenter went into orbit, each for a period of four and a half hours. Still later, Schirra orbited the earth nearly six times, for approximately nine hours in space.

The addition for comparisons was simple. Gherman Titov remained in space for a period of time considerably greater than that of Shepard, Grissom, Glenn, Carpenter, and Schirra combined. But between the orbiting of Carpenter and Schirra something else had happened. That was the brilliant dual flight of Nikolayev (four days in orbit) and Popovich (three days in orbit). The staggering complexity of this dual space mission has not yet been impressed upon the American public. The basic accomplishment itself is many years advanced over anything this nation can effect in space or even plans to attempt. For nowhere in the plans of the United States in its space programs for this decade will you find a project that calls for the simultaneous orbiting and rendezvous in space of two manned ships.

The flight of astronaut Wally Schirra for not quite six orbits of the earth has been hailed as a spectacular scientific feat. Compared to what we had accomplished in manned space flight until that moment, it was a great triumph. And we claimed that it was because of this flight that the Mercury capsule was at long last completely vindicated. It could be kept in orbit under drifting flight, without the need for constant attitude corrections, so that the astronaut might conserve his precious supply of fuel.

Imagine the staggering accomplishment of the Russians by not only proving this same thing, but by going ahead with all the other aspects of their dual manned flight. The cosmonauts breathed air maintained at sea-level pressure and with sea-level constituents; our astronauts must breathe pure oxygen at less than six pounds per square inch pressure. The Mercury capsule has about as much room as a telephone booth; the Russians unstrapped themselves and moved about their cabins. They carried food, water, power, control and other supplies sufficient for a mission of at least twelve days in space. They were monitored by dual television cameras in each spaceship. They performed a bewildering variety of military, engineering, and scientific tasks.

The level of scientific calculations and computer engineering for these flights has earned the profound admiration of scientists in the field even if it has escaped the general public and the men who prepare press releases to compare our manned space flight program to that of the Soviets. Because of minor errors ("errors" *we* consider as being "smack on target") in the launching of Vostok III, the Russians were forced to perform a near-miracle of computer engineering in order to re-plan the launching and flight of the second spaceship, Vostok IV. Computer scientists in the United States have described the subsequent orbiting as "as neat a job of two objects in the same place at the same velocity in the same plane at the same altitude at the same time" as one might imagine. In order to bring the two Vostoks close together—within 1.87 miles of each other—the second spaceship had to be launched within a "window" measured in seconds. Reliability of equipment had to be better than superb. It had to be, and it was, as close to perfection as possible.

Based on the calculations made by American scientists, using American tracking data, Dr. Martin Summerfield, Professor of Aeronautical Engineering at Princeton University, said that the Russian shot was: "Remarkable! Real pickle-barrel shooting!"

It is the United States that for the past several years has hammered repeatedly at the theme that rendezvous missions in earth orbit will affect profoundly the capabilities of any nation. We consider—and we have again and again stated—that rendezvous is the key to an extraordinary variety of missions. We are basing much of our future advances in space upon the concept of orbital rendezvous and docking.

We do not attempt to plan a rendezvous mission—between a 7,000-pound Gemini spacecraft and an unmanned Agena-D rocket —until the fourth or fifth mission in the Gemini program. Gemini will not get into orbit until 1964 at the earliest, and the rendezvous mission (unless there is an urgent priority effort to speed up the program) will not occur until 1965.

A comparison is not difficult. Our program calls for the initial placement of the manned spaceship in orbit within a distance of some twenty miles of the rendezvous target. This is considered to be superb guidance and accuracy and we hope to bring about this feat in 1965. The Russians brought two spaceships into orbital rendezvous in the fall of 1962.

To consider this matter of comparisons one step further, it is interesting to match timetables of accomplishment.

We trailed the Soviet Union by *four months* in the launching of the first space satellite, but with a satellite that matched the Russian vehicle "in spirit only."

We trailed the Russians by *ten months* in sending our first man into orbit in a spaceship that weighed some seven thousand pounds less than the Soviet craft.

If our timetable holds for our first attempted 24-hour orbiting of an astronaut, in June of 1963, we will accomplish this feat some *twenty-one months* after the Russians kept a man in space for 25 hours.

If our timetable holds for our first rendezvous mission in space in 1965, but with only one of the two spacecraft being manned, we will bring about this feat some *thirty to thirty-six months* after the Russian rendezvous mission. If this is proof that we are "catching up" with the Russians it is a strange proof, indeed.

There are a host of reasons for the grim determination of the Russians to perfect orbital rendezvous and docking. First, of course, it will provide the means to assemble huge payloads in orbit about the earth. Through orbital rendezvous it is possible to place enormous, permanently manned stations in orbit, to be employed for scientific, military, and research purposes and to act as the intermediate stations for flights from the earth to the moon.

An exhaustive study of orbital rendezvous led the Congress to note in a special report:

> The accomplishment of orbital rendezvous would be a convincing demonstration of our ability to go where and when we wish in space, and would be the measure by which we could make realizable plans for almost any future space application.
>
> Orbital rendezvous would find useful payoffs in the operation of advanced communications, weather, and other reconnaissance systems; it would allow the maintenance of permanent laboratories in space; it would allow the mounting of versatile expeditions to other natural bodies in space; *and it would lie at the heart of most military space operations* ...

And at this moment the United States does *not* have (1) a military manned space flight program, and (2) any military program encompassing manned vehicles for rendezvous operations. We do have paper plans, which are "being studied extensively."

Responding to the implications of increasing superiority of the Soviet Union in military space systems as a result of the successful dual flight of the Vostoks in August 1962, Senator Howard W. Cannon warned that this mission provides "stark evidence" not only of Russian intentions but also of Russian capabilities toward reaching the goal of "attaining military dominance in the near-earth space envelope."

The remarks of Senator Cannon should have special emphasis for they reflected not only his views, but also represented a wide cross-section of military and scientific authorities, who will speak freely enough behind closed doors, but not before the public.

Those "closed door" sessions left absolutely no doubt, warned the Senator, that no matter to what extent the National Aeronautics and Space Administration pursues orbital rendezvous, the very great divergence of requirements between civilian and military space operations precludes meeting military necessity through "civilian space missions." It is because of this crippling separation between requirements and missions that "the present direction of our national efforts in space gives little or no assurance that attention is truly directed to the development of our military capabilities."

In his 1960 campaign statements, President Kennedy drew special attention to the fact that: "If the Soviets control space, they can control the earth . . . The U.S. must have pre-eminence in security as an umbrella under which we can explore and develop space."

Several years later, we lacked even the blueprints from which we might begin to build the umbrella.

Generals Schriever and White, as well as other knowledgeable authorities, have emphasized that the military space mission must be based upon certain accepted capabilities: the aerospace force must function on the hard foundation of readiness, responsiveness to command, and adaptability to national needs and policies.

Those items are standards in the military field. In their application to a space force they establish requirements which do not find much compatibility with the needs of nonmilitary exploration and exploitation of space. Any military vehicle must be, as much as possible, simple, reliable, and flexible. The only thing in common between the civilian space vehicle and the military is the matter of reliability. Above all, the civilian vehicle does not require responsiveness to command.

It is necessary to fire a research payload, under certain conditions, at specific times. But the countdown leading to that time is measured with exquisite care and attention to detail. The shot is affected by weather, by any one of a thousand details which cannot interfere with a military vehicle. Any military manned space operation must be ready to go and must not be restrictively responsive to weather, tracking radar, data acquisition instruments, and so forth. This is not a deprecation of the scientific mission because of its vastly increased complexity and sensitivity, but a statement of fact. By virtue of its requirements and goals, the scientific mission must function as a finicky, hypersensitive, and problem-plagued operation. The need is for the perfection of operation of thousands of separate items, each of which justifies the mission through its accumulation of data.

The military requirement may be wrapped up neatly within a single package: fulfill the mission. The military requirement, in the words of Brockway McMillan, Assistant Secretary of the Air Force for Research and Development, is *not:* ". . . a product with the greatest mass fraction or the lightest autopilot, or the most transistors, but a product that does what it is supposed to do when it is supposed to do it when it is called upon to do it, without the tender, loving care of a hundred technicians for six weeks."

Even more to the point is the ability of the manned space system to conduct orbital operations keyed to flexibility. There is the essential requirement of responding not to specific situations, but to circumstances which are impossible to predict. Any military system must retain as the core of its structure what engineers fondly refer to as "the ultimate difference between man and machine—the power of decision."

Unless the manned space systems this country is developing integrate this goal in their design and development, our expenditure of billions of dollars and years of effort will produce interesting research vehicles for the manned exploration of space; vehicles that will inherently be cumbersome, unwieldy, inflexible, and condemned to operations within the narrowest of performance margins.

Unless we develop now the systems that permit flexibility, change of orbit, maneuverability within orbit, freedom of re-entry, freedom of control during re-entry, choice of landing sites with great flexibility; unless all these things and more are begun now, then, as Mr. McMillan has commented wryly, all our spacemen will be able to accomplish in meeting national needs in space "is to carry the flag."

Despite the attempts of a small castigated minority, our venture into space is not something of which we can be exceptionally proud nor will history treat us kindly in this respect. It is not pleasant to realize that our participation springs from a reaction to the leadership of another nation rather than from a desire to lead the way.

Although we have sent dozens of satellites into space, our record is not commendable. Our role in tomorrow's world will be decided not so much by the number of satellites, but in the policies we have established to determine our conduct in space. We have become embroiled in what Mr. I. A. Getting, President of Aerospace Corporation, describes with deep feeling as a space dichotomy—a situation in which the United States wraps itself in a cloak of unreality. The unreality is so obvious that we seem to have a psychological compulsion to avoid it. We reaffirm that there really is not one kind, but two distinct and separate kinds, of space exploration. One is peaceful, scientific and pure; the other is military, evil, and even maniacal.

Mr. Getting notes with misgivings that: "In thus assuming that there is a space dichotomy—that somehow our space activities can be split into good and evil parts—we create an artificial, false situation that hurts us both at home and around the world. . . . Let me note that throughout history, very often it has been the professional military man who in peacetime has braved the frontiers of the unknown and pushed them back."

The journey of Christopher Columbus was a military expedition, carried out under military orders. The expedition in 1804 of Lewis and Clark—and fourteen soldiers—was a military mission assigned the nonmilitary task of exploring the virgin territories acquired by the Louisiana Purchase. And not only on this expedition, but on many others, men carried out their duties by fighting the unknown, struggling across mountains and plains, fording rivers and deserts, preparing the charts and the maps that would permit the passage of others who were to follow behind. These were missions of a military nature—but their purpose was not to fight.

Far and away the majority of the pioneering in flight has been carried out by the military. Navy pilots and crews were the first to cross the Atlantic in 1919. Five years later a group of Army pilots and crews performed feats of unbelievable skill and heroism in the first aerial circumnavigation of this planet. When the National Geographic Society set for itself the then-awesome goal of conducting an aerial expedition to the Arctic in 1925, there was no question but that we would rely upon the military. And so the flying contingent for this great exploration came from the Navy, and was led by Admiral Richard E. Byrd.

The first extensive scientific explorations by Americans of the stratosphere and beyond were military expeditions in balloons. The first exploration into the barrier reefs of supersonic flight was made by a military officer in a military craft. We are proud of each and every such venture, performed for us by men in uniform whose thoughts and goals were not of fighting other men but of the dangers and hazards that lay before them. We are proud today of the extensive operations by our scientists in the study of the Antarctic. Virtually all of this scientific investigation and conquest has been conducted by a great military force.

It is not only in exploration that we have entrusted our national stature to the military services. There is the matter of scientific research and study conducted on a vast scale in thousands of laboratories and universities; in airplanes carrying instruments for the study of cosmic radiation; in experiments to produce new computers—to gain some added comprehension of the mysteries of this earth and of our universe.

The building of the Panama Canal was a military venture. Not quite a hundred years back in our history, we cheered the use of four military vessels, two American and two British, to lay the first telegraphic cable across the Atlantic.

As Mr. Getting points out:

> No one batted an eye over this employment of naval strength for a peaceful purpose.
>
> ... Why is it that in space matters alone this confusion exists—in the United States but certainly not in the USSR— this misunderstanding that there is a dichotomy, an artificial division between military activities on the one hand and all other activities for peaceful purposes on the other? Why do we associate exploration and science only with a civilian agency and deny these to the military? Why do we place an evil cast on military activities in space?

There is no question, if we are interested in assuring our continued survival in the future, that we must abandon this connotation of "evil" with military space exploration. For we were host to the same kind of mental rubbish in the past. In 1903 the Wright Brothers conducted their first successful flight. But five years before this historic occasion, the Hague Peace Conference solemnly declared that no aircraft, either existing or projected, was ever to be used in a fashion that would aid in the prosecution of a war.

Agreement was reached among the attending nations that aircraft were to be used only passively—for reconnaissance and surveillance.

Does it have a similar ring to the language we are employing today? We will be no more successful in our current fumbling attempts to escape the inevitable military role in space than were the members of the Hague Peace Conference in terms of aircraft back in 1898. Nine years later, in 1907, in the Second Hague Conference, the smell of war was in the air, and airplanes were now a reality rather than a chicken-wire-and-fabric dream. Of the forty-four nations attending the Second Hague Conference, twenty-seven reaffirmed the ban on dropping explosives and projectiles from aircraft. Of the twenty-seven, the majority were small nations for which the prospects of aerial units of any consequence were so dim that their opinions were of academic interest only. The United States, as might be expected, was the nation that led the group to a reaffirmation of the promises *never* to employ aircraft for combat purposes.

Mr. Getting observes:

> Are we being realistic in trying to save space for "peace"? Have we sold the idea to others? Or are we fooling principally ourselves? It would appear that a chief argument for preserving space for peaceful purposes is somehow connected with the sanctity of space.
>
> ... There is no substantial evidence from history that any power in time of national danger has denied itself the use of any medium when it considered the use of that medium to its advantage. Today space has more potential for the free world than for the communist world—but in the exploitation of space *we appear to be risking unilateral disarmament.*
>
> I might insert here the comment that somehow we have espoused space for peaceful purposes with the implication that the earth should be reserved for warlike purposes.
>
> [Since 1958 the] de-emphasis of the Air Force conduct

of—not merely participation in—U.S. space experiments resulted in very real damage to the morale and, in my opinion,
the thoroughly proper, thoroughly legitimate mission of the
military to help keep the peace.

If anything, there has been a steady, further erosion of
military morale in the years since then, and I fear greatly
that the inevitable consequence to the national welfare will
be significant. If this damage to military morale and military
effectiveness were the price that had to be paid to earn worldwide respect in a new era of international goodwill, perhaps
the cost would be justified. But I have seen no evidence that
the dawn of this new era of understanding has come. . . .

There is a factor which few Americans consider: the astronauts
who led the way into space for the United States are military personnel. They are fighter pilots and test pilots. Some of them have
fought in war. John Glenn fought not in one, but in two. Our
Government lauded and decorated these men. Today, as military
pilots, they are governed by military orders, are paid according
to their rank, and accrue time toward promotion in rank. For
their assignments as astronauts, they are on "detached duty" to
the NASA. As combat-trained, combat-experienced military pilots,
they will later return to their respective services.

But when is the last time we have seen these men in their
uniforms? When they appeared before the Congress, their uniforms
were hidden. When they appear before the press, it is not in the
uniforms they have worn so proudly for so many years. Why are
we so ashamed of that uniform that these men are directed to
wear civilian clothes when appearing in public?

If there is one conclusion we might reach after the first five
years of space exploration it is the feeling of dismay that our one-
sided and blind adherence to Marquis of Queensbury rules will
yet be the death of us.

CHAPTER 13.

A SENSE OF URGENCY

IT is time to evaluate our accomplishments as a nation in space exploration. What we have achieved during these past five years will, in fair measure, provide a yardstick for what we may hope to achieve in the next five to ten years. This measurement should not be taken in the number of satellites we have lofted, for this is often misleading, let alone meaningless. It is easy to find charts of comparison that show the total number of American satellites in orbit—often three, four, or five times as many as those rocketed into space by the Soviets.

Yet the purpose of a satellite is to produce information, and many of these robot messengers to which we refer are mute, their electronic voices stricken by time, by radiation floods in space, and by mechanical failure. And there are some satellites in their looping paths about this planet that, after months and even years, amaze us with the shrill durability of their electronic cries. If you study another list, it will show you the number of such robots that continue to chatter madly from space; and the number will be emphasized with pride. Too often, however, you will not see the despair of the scientists who wish for some cord with which they might strangle the electronic chatterboxes; for the satellites broadcast, but not the desired information.

Because our limited airways for data transmitted down from space require careful apportioning, we build cutoff times into the radio transmitters. At a specific time, memory units command the satellite to shut up. Sometimes, those memory units or their controls snarl in the operation, or they forget to remember, and the satellite resembles a magpie in the vacuum of space, with a strident voice that is the bane of the men preparing new experiments.

Unfortunately, what the American public sees and reads more often than not is the product of a carefully contrived comparison that miraculously avoids realities and paints a picture of superiority on our part. We are quick to show what our small, scientific satellites have accomplished, and we are even quicker to claim that our activities in space are more rewarding than those of the Russians.

For example, we have established beyond a doubt in anyone's mind that the work we have accomplished in meteorological satellites is the only work of its kind in space. Our Tiros robots have performed in excellent fashion, and they have presented us the scientific rewards of tens of thousands of outstanding photographs of the weather patterns on this planet.

In 1962 the Soviet Union sent into space thirteen Cosmos satellites. They were, so far as we may determine, satellites crammed with scientific instruments and equipment. They were placed in orbits well suited to extensive scientific research. The Cosmos satellite series began four years after the orbiting of Sputnik III back in the spring of 1958.

How big are the Cosmos satellites? One may assume at least as big as the Vostok spaceships. And those weigh more than ten thousand pounds. But why stop at this figure, since in February of 1961 the Russians were orbiting payloads exceeding fourteen thousand pounds in weight.

The public does not know the size and the weight of these satellites, but our Government does know. It tracks these satellites. It takes excellent photographs of them in orbit. It photographs the boosters. It determines the weight of the satellite by noting the speed at which the orbits decay, and because we know orbital decay figures, we can extrapolate the weight of the Russian satellites.

And what of the payload within these satellites? If our sources are correct—and they do not constitute guesswork—those Cosmos satellites weigh about seventeen thousand pounds each.

On June 19, 1962, the United States sent Tiros V into orbit. Our meteorological satellite weighed 286 pounds. Each Cosmos satellite weighs *sixty times* as much as a Tiros satellite. How many cameras are maintained in the Cosmos satellites? We don't know. Do the Russians have television transmission from space, as we do with Tiros? Of course they do—they have been using live television transmission for years. What is packed inside the Cosmos satellites? We don't know.

When we make our comparisons which appear as tidy charts and columns of figures in our newspapers, those comparisons are based in large part upon great and significant gaps in the available information. We simply don't know, and the Russians haven't seen fit to tell us.

So, are we ahead of the Soviets in meteorological satellites, in navigation satellites, in communications and other satellites? We certainly have proven no superiority in guidance—one need only glance at the dismal record of our probes to the moon to find a ready conclusion available. We have absolutely nothing on which to base a premise of superiority in electronics. And in reliability? We have quite a distance to travel before we will match the Russians in reliability. We lack the weight in our satellites for the kind of capacity we need and find so appealing in Russian satellites. We've got to miniaturize and subminiaturize, and build our components with incredible sensitivity and fragility.

There is another flaw in this repetition of scientific satellite superiority we have taken so greatly to heart. The key to the successful exploitation of space will never lie in the intricate, expensive, balky, unreliable black boxes of robot vehicles. The key to success and superiority on a long-range basis lies in the man-machine system, a combination of the best of the two.

There is no question but that the Russians are moving just as quickly as their impressive capabilities will allow them to do, in order to create a powerful and reliable system of manned space vehicles.

The Russians have struck out for the long pull. They have bent every effort to achieve this goal above all others. They have not, in the process, ignored scientific requirements, as may be attested to in their Sputniks, their lunar probes, their shots to Mars and to Venus, and in their Cosmos series. But everything has pounded along inexorably toward a clearly defined goal.

It is our position that we have reaped fabulous rewards in scientific data in our space explorations. This is true. It is so obvious that it is almost painful. We are proud of our willingness to share what we learn from our experiments with scientific satellites. In keeping with the grandiose gesture we made to the world—our promise to share our wealth of information—we print thick reports crammed with the results of our experiments. It is a noble move. Scientists of other nations approve heartily of this effort on our part. Especially the scientists of the USSR.

What a wonderful situation! The Russians must concentrate more on the manned systems of space flight in order to reach their goal, than on flurries of smaller scientific satellites sent into space. But Russians need to be as inquisitive as anyone else. Before a nation may begin to establish a means of controlling space, it is necessary to accumulate extensive knowledge of the space environment. Knowledge of any virgin territory is priceless. The Russians want to know the kind of information we are reaping. They would like to see the photographs taken by Tiros, and study the records of meteorological events. They are interested in the results of our navigation satellite tests, and they'd like to use those results for their own navigation needs.

They'd like all these things, and we are obliging. We tell the Russians in exorbitant detail just what we do out there and how we do it. We supply the raw data, the methods of breaking down this data, and we supply in exquisite detail the final results. At this point they don't even need a program of weather satellites. We give them everything we know.

They want to use navigation systems based on Transit satellites. And we oblige here too. We publish the frequencies and the orbital data, and anyone can use them. How about the details of our communications satellites? They are free. The Russians may be getting a bit swaybacked as they carry off the thick reports, but this constitutes the extent of their labors in this area.

We are engaged in the most astounding, unbelievable giveaway in the history of this planet.

There is a saying that the United States should erect a monument to Sputnik I. It broke the chains of lethargy and swept aside the disrepute in which we held ventures into space. Perhaps the Russians will also erect a monument. To us. If so, it may well be that this monument will be in the form of an enormous pile of official documents on research in space.

We must remind ourselves over and over that national attitudes produce national policies. And policy is both the avenue on which we travel into space, and also a measure of the effort we exert in determining the speed of our travels. How fast do we move into space scientifically or otherwise? Our space program is one of reaction, as we have learned, rather than one of initiative on our own part. But before one can react, there must be knowledge of the challenge and how strong that challenge may be. This means an evaluation of the opponent in the race.

In 1961, Dr. T. Keith Glennan, the NASA Administrator, was called before a Congressional Committee to present an evaluation of American *vs.* Soviet space sciences. Dr. Glennan stated candidly:

The average quality of Soviet scientific research is the same as that of the United States. This conclusion is based on perusal of their literature and on personal contacts between scientists of both countries in conferences held between 1956 and 1960, both in nuclear physics and in areas related to space research.

The range of ability of Soviet scientists is also approximately the same as that of U.S. scientists. A few are brilliant, as good as this nation's best physicists, and the majority do conventional but necessary research.

And then Dr. Glennan continued with one of the most remarkable processes of evaluation known. He called particular attention to the fact that—

Another significant fact appears in the comparison of United States and U.S.S.R. papers published in the periodical literature or presented at international conferences: The United States and U.S.S.R. papers are of comparable quality but the number of U.S. papers greatly exceeds the U.S.S.R. contribution. This very sizable discrepancy in the level of effort constitutes the most significant difference between the United States and U.S.S.R. space research programs.

This may be one of the more significant contributions to the exploration of space. On the basis of the number of scientific papers presented at congenial international meetings we have prepared a yardstick that allows us to conclude, in our favor, a "significant difference between the United States and USSR space research programs. . . ."

This presupposes two premises. The first is that the weight and volume of scientific papers really does constitute an accurate and meaningful yardstick for evaluating a space program, and, second, that the Soviet Union has placed a maximum effort into the production of these paper reports. Thus we may further conclude that the Russians have told us everything they are doing in space, in complete and absolutely honest detail, but that they really aren't "up to it," and that we reign supreme in the scientific study of the space environment.

At the moment that Dr. Glennan presented this remarkable system of evaluation to the Committee, the United States had prepared an extraordinary bulk of scientific papers on the moon. It was unfortunate, but nevertheless it was a fact, that the content of these papers remained essentially conjecture. Conjecture remained all we had because of our poor record in attempting to remove some of the mystery from the moon. That record, at the time, included the expenditure of three Thor-Able, two Juno II, and four great Atlas-Able rockets, each of which had been assigned the mission of sending scientific payloads to the vicinity of the moon, or of landing upon the lunar surface.

Of these nine rockets, one exploded on its launching pad days before its scheduled moment of launch. Two others exploded in the air shortly after they rose from their launch stands. Three suffered in-flight failures that doomed them to blazing incineration in the earth's atmosphere. Two lofted out into space to a distance of about one-fourth of the way to the moon, and then fell back to burn to ashes in our atmosphere. One little probe, weighing 13 pounds, sailed past the moon at so great a distance (37,300 miles) that its instrument package was simply not up to the task of carrying out any investigations.

But we did have extensive, thick, detailed, and elaborate scientific papers on the study of the moon. By contrast, the Russian presentation of their lunar studies program did not approach the size, bulk or weight of the American papers. This is true—despite the passage of a heavy Russian probe past the moon at 3,200 miles; the impact of an even heavier Russian probe against the lunar surface; and a swing around the moon with a third probe. The results of the latter were presented in a slim sheaf of papers, but they did contain photographs of the far side of the moon. The remainder of the Russian presentation was concerned essentially with the findings of the instruments that had been sent, quite successfully, to the moon.

Later, when he referred to the "geodetic application of satellites," Dr. Glennan reaffirmed his position by noting that there "has been relatively little U.S.S.R. work published on this important and interesting problem."

Dr. Glennan then added some qualification to these conclusions, when he noted that, "It is possible that this particular field of geodesy is considered sensitive by the Russians, and that for this reason a substantial amount of U.S.S.R. material has been held back from publication."

There is unanimous agreement among scientists, politicians, engineers, educators, philosophers—the entire spectrum of national leaders in every walk of life—that the technological, scientific, economic gains (to name a few) from space exploration will determine which nation will in the future reign as the undisputed leader of the world. They will determine, also, which nation will be clearly defined as a second-rate power.

Realizing the extent of the challenge, the deep significance of the rewards, the grim dangers of failure—how has this country, through the organization established by the Congress, met and coped with these many challenges? Perhaps we have not done nearly as well as we would lead people to believe . . .

A disturbed Congressional Committee * drew attention to the fact that the American space effort—

> . . . appeared to be lagging in certain very crucial phases including propulsion.
>
> In spite of successful satellite launchings and missile advances, in spite of valuable data collection, reduction and interpretation by U.S. science teams—an astronautic endeavor possibly unequalled elsewhere in the world—it was obvious that the American effort was beset with growing pains, doubts,

* House Report No. 2092 of the Committee on Science and Astronautics, July 5, 1960.

and some indecision. This may have been a normal condition under the circumstances, but if so it was nonetheless a risky one in view of the apparent stakes involved.

Chairman Overton Brooks: "Those of us on this Committee would be indulging in fanciful thinking if we did not admit to ourselves that the U.S. space effort has reached neither the pace nor the proportions which we had hoped for when we passed the National Aeronautics and Space Act in July 1958. Perhaps we expected too much. But there are definite indications—these have existed some time—that a true sense of urgency has not constantly attended the American space program."

[The Committee Report concluded that—] One of the things that have been troubling people is whether the space program is being pushed with a deep enough sense of urgency, or whether it is proceeding generally on a business-as-usual basis.

Three of the most important programs in America's space effort to catch up with and surpass the Soviet Union are Project Mercury, Project Saturn, and Nova. . . . Neither the testimony given this committee by NASA officials nor other facts available to it would indicate that the three programs were pushed with sufficient urgency.

One year later the situation apparently had changed little— if at all. A Committee member with ill-concealed frustration reminded NASA officials that while a sense of urgency seemed to be absent from NASA it was not missing from the Congress:

Some of us have this feeling of urgency and really a feeling of frustration, and try to say: "Tell us what you need. Broaden it ahead of time, and let us hear what it is, and we will help you get it." Time after time we come up against a new problem and say we are doing the best we can. It seems to me that it is all happening after the expected event, rather than before.

If there is any way that we on this Committee can give

you successful alternatives and give you added components, added equipment, added test stands, or added test facilities, out in private business, I wish you would come up and say it to us. I think we in the United States are not only losing space, but we are losing the imagination of the young people of this world.

They are beginning to think that Russia is first in everything. Once these people of the world that are not committed begin to think Russia is first—militarily, as well as in all of science—you can have all the conferences and summit meetings you want, and let me tell you we are at the bottom of the summit and they are at the top before we begin.

I wish you people . . . would have a feeling that you are vital to the security of this country. And that it is much more than just going along with an adequate ten-year program. So that some of us are worried about it. We seem to be pressing here, want to give you the opportunity and want to give you the facilities really to do the job. What do you need more to do it and get on with it?

I get very frustrated about it. . . .

When the budget department simply says "No," you seem to accept it rather than going either higher in the administration or come over to Congress and tell us quickly.

. . . at some point in time we are going to have to cut through a lot of this Peter-to-Paul-and-back-again business and get quick decisions without too many levels of authority; because to me in the space program there are too many who can say "No," and too few people who can say "Yes." You are running into Noes very quietly and accepting them. . . .

CHAPTER **14.**

20–20 MYOPIA

IN the early days of America's struggle to build a civilian organization for the exploration of space, an unwanted stepchild
skulked around the back doors of our space program. In our plans
to launch satellites, there was little place for man. An astonishing
number of scientists curled their upper lips and tried to be rid
of this aggravating fellow. Man could do very little in space. He
was an annoyance that the scientists wished would simply go away.

This seems difficult if not impossible to believe when we recall
the frenzied hysteria of millions of screaming, adoring people
who lined the streets for astronaut John Glenn on his return to
earth from several hours in orbit. In fact, at such a time it seemed
hard to believe that there was anything else not directly associated
with man going on in our space program.

But the scientists still curled their lips and bemoaned the un-
tutored interference of the unqualified. And again they reiterated
their desires to be left alone so that they might putter about with
their shiny and expensive robot equipment.

One of our most eminent and respected of all scientists, Dr.
Vannevar Bush, spoke for them when he informed the Congress
in 1960 that:

Putting a man in space is a stunt; the man can do no more than an instrument, in fact can do less. The days when men will be in space for long periods and for varied purposes, are so far off that we need not hurry on one aspect of their reactions and potential operations. There are far more serious things to do than to indulge in stunts. As yet the American people do not understand the distinctions, and we in this country are prone to rush, for a time, at any new thing. I do not discard completely the value of demonstrating to the world our skills. Nor do I undervalue the effect on morale of the spectacular. But the present hullabaloo on the propaganda aspects of the program leaves me entirely cool.

This is the sort of thing that upsets legislators who pass laws authorizing billions of dollars for programs to send men into space. Comments such as those of Dr. Bush, who not too many years before his stand on this subject had ridiculed the proposition of a long-range ballistic missile, made Congress think that it might be wise to have a meticulous study of the man-in-space matter.

The Biosciences Advisory Committee, under the direction of Dr. Seymour S. Kety, was formed of seven distinguished scientists. Their report is extraordinarily important. It slices away the propaganda and the proposals bulging with grandiose schemes. It reduces the subject to its true meaning. It is invaluable to an understanding of why men will, and must, accept the problems and the hazards of exploration beyond this world:

> The basic study of extraterrestrial environments is ultimately likely to be most productive in furthering an understanding of the fundamental laws of nature. Among the most perplexing questions which have challenged men's minds are the nature and origin of life and the possibility of its presence elsewhere in the universe than on the earth alone. For the first time in history, partial answers to these questions are within reach. . . . These studies will not be complete until the scientist himself is able to make meticulous investigations on the spot.

This is true, not only for the biological, but, also, for many other physical, chemical and geological problems which are involved. Although significant engineering achievements in automation, sensing, recording, programming and telemetering have been realized and considerable future development is in prospect, the indispensability of the human observer in much of space exploration is well established. Man's versatility and selectivity, his ability to perceive the significance of unexpected and unprogrammed findings or to react intelligently to unanticipated situations have not been simulated by any combination of physical devices, however complex, which have been developed or are even contemplated. Human intelligence and manual skill in servicing the complicated mechanisms of space vehicles or repairing breakdowns in flight are not readily dispensed with or replaced. When along with these attributes are considered his weight of 70 kg. [154 pounds], his total resting power requirements of 100 watts, his ability to function for years without maintenance or breakdown, then even the most elaborate provisions for his sustenance, welfare and safety are amply justified simply in terms of engineering efficiency. A national program in space which does not recognize the essentiality of the human observer and does not plan to utilize him most effectively may wait indefinitely for the automatic devices to replace him or be limited to incomplete and opportunistic observations.

The report of this eminent scientific panel may be said to represent the official policy of the United States. The United States committed a great effort—with a cost of more than five hundred million dollars—to get a man into orbit in a lumpish, 3,000-pound space capsule. Project Mercury is a household word. The seven Mercury astronauts are national heroes and they are the recipients of speeches, awards, parades, gifts, and lush commercial contracts. Project Mercury, with its astronauts, is synonymous with America in space, and it is also the best known effort of NASA. It is our civilian program to establish men in orbit about this planet, to accumulate the knowledge with which we can plan future manned efforts.

Despite all the words and convictions to the contrary, Project Mercury is not our civilian manned space program and it is not a creation of NASA. Neither did this program begin in 1958 after the creation of NASA; it was under way at least two years before this time. Only it was then known by a different name—*Project 7969*. In March of 1956 the United States Air Force initiated Project 7969 and entitled this venture its "Manned Ballistic Rocket Research System." Project 7969 was given a specific task: recover a manned capsule from orbital conditions.

By December of 1956, the Air Force received from two industrial firms with which it was negotiating, clear-cut proposals to conduct the program. But in 1956 "space" was not yet respectable, and funds were critically short. Unable to contract the work to be done, the Air Force initiated extensive in-house studies among its own personnel and facilities. Simultaneously, Air Force officials laid it right on the line to industry. The explanation was short and simple: we need certain work and we can't afford to pay you any money. Will you finance the necessary research studies with your own corporate funds?

It is amazing how responsive industry is to such queries. By January of 1958, the Air Force was studying seven firm proposals from different industrial organizations on their manner of developing an orbital vehicle. At this point the Air Force moved shoulder to shoulder with scientists of the National Advisory Committee for Aeronautics, and began a severe technical evaluation of the concepts submitted. While this progressed, NACA scientists studied the possibilities of utilizing the ballistic missile booster, that is, Atlas, to provide the required velocity, height, and control to place a manned capsule in low earth orbit. These studies began in 1956, and were intensified in 1957 and 1958.

On January 31, 1958, the Air Force, in a formal letter to the

Director of NACA, invited NACA participation in the manned orbital flight program of the Air Force. On April 11, 1958, an agreement in writing for such coordinated effort was received.

During this period the Air Force had not yet received clear and official authority for such a program. This came in February of 1958 from the Advanced Research Projects Agency (ARPA). An ARPA memorandum dated February 28, 1958, clearly stated that "ARPA recognized the Air Force has a long-term development responsibility for manned space flight capability, with the primary objective of accomplishing satellite flight as soon as technology permits." The memorandum further "authorized development of a test vehicle for experimental flights with laboratory animals, in furtherance of the objective of manned satellite flight."

At last the Air Force was officially in the manned space business. Unfortunately, its tenure in office was to be brief. By March of 1958 NACA forwarded its recommendations that "the first manned satellites should be ballistic entry vehicles launched with existing intercontinental ballistic missile propulsion systems." As NACA worked on the fine details of the vehicles, work went on rapidly and concurrently in the mutually supporting areas of development.

Brigadier General Don Flickinger, Assistant for Bioastronautics, Headquarters, Air Research and Development Command, explained:

> Prior to October of 1957 we had done a considerable amount of biomedical work studying the problems of manned space flight. Immediately after Sputnik we directed our efforts toward the development of a single manned ballistic capsule which shortly was expanded to comprise the Air Force man-in-space program. Under direction from the Advanced Research Projects Agency, this program was reduced in scope, shortened in time, and renamed Man in Space Soonest (MISS).

The Air Force completed their 7969 proposal in extensive detail. The Atlas ICBM would be mated with a suitable upper stage so that a large and heavy manned capsule could be placed into orbit. There would be facilities for biomedical, engineering and scientific experiments in orbit. When the time came to return to earth, the pilot, after positioning the capsule to its specific attitude, would fire retrorockets to break his orbit and begin his ballistic descent. During the period of atmospheric re-entry, radio beacons and other aids would be activated for purposes of search and recovery and the capsule would descend beneath a large parachute. Initially, the Air Force planned for descents into the ocean in the Caribbean. There were further details, and as these became firm the program evolved to develop a capsule that would permit the pilot to remain in orbit for at least twenty-four hours.

The Air Force meant to gain extensive experience in equipment and procedures by conducting major research programs before the manned capsule would be ready for flight. They intended to develop small recoverable satellites and work up along the scale until the full-sized ballistic capsule itself was used for orbiting and recovery from orbit.

This is where the Discoverer series came into play. Prior to the time that the Air Force received official authorization for MISS, it had developed the small recoverable satellites as part of Discoverer. Mice and then small primates would go into the capsules.

Following this initial series of animal experiments, the Discoverer satellites would be equipped with middle-sized packages. To create the Thor-Agena booster, the Air Force developed an upper stage rocket by using the propulsion system from its B-58 Hustler bomber. The supersonic bomber carried a propulsion pod into combat areas, launching this weapon while still far from its target. The engine from this pod met the needs of the Discoverer program perfectly and Agena was born.

With the Discoverer series well along, orbiting chimpanzees for several hours and then for several days, the Air Force planned to integrate the Atlas booster into the program as quickly as it would become available. The first flights into orbit with the Atlas were to be with heavily instrumented, unmanned capsules. Next would come flights with the larger primates and, finally, the first flight with a man. North American Aviation, Inc. built two complete mockups of the capsule, and the General Electric Company received the contract to proceed with development of the life support system.

Does all this have a familiar ring to it? Does this sound like a description of the civilian manned space program known as Project Mercury? It should because it is Project Mercury.

In October of 1958, the Congress handed NASA the ball with instructions to run just as rapidly as possible for the successful accomplishments of the goals of Project Mercury. In the years that followed, the Congress found itself less than enchanted with the progress it saw in Project Mercury, and in a restrained admonishment of NASA, noted in July of 1960 that "Project Mercury . . . progress was comparatively slow."

Behind the scenes, Mercury did not enjoy the sense of urgency which the country generally believed was present in our effort to accomplish manned space flight. Although within NASA itself there could be detected something less than urgent and priority development, the fault could be traced clearly to the vast Government structure itself.

On November 14, 1958, NASA formally submitted a request for a DX priority, the highest industrial priority in the country, for Project Mercury. The National Aeronautics and Space Council, headed by the Vice President, acted on the request several weeks later. The Space Council officially rejected the DX priority request for Mercury thus assuring that the program would be subjected to slippages caused by greater emphasis on other programs.

On December 9, 1958, the Civilian-Military Liaison Committee recommended to both NASA and the Department of Defense that the DX priority immediately be made effective for Mercury. With this recommendation came some hard arguments, notably this one:

> ... many of the items which would be critical to the rate of progress of Project Mercury (including assignment of production boosters, use of test facilities, and operational services such as launching, tracking, etc.) were items required by several military projects already carrying a DX rating. It was the consensus that absence of a DX rating would thus almost certainly mean delay in getting a man into space.

Despite the urgency of the arguments for top priority for Mercury, the Space Council refused to take immediate action. Finally, on April 27, 1959, it did approve the DX priority rating for Project Mercury. On April 30 the Department of Defense received notification of this action. And a week later (May 5, 1959), a year and a half after the Russians first went into space, Mercury received its DX priority.

The year following, the Congress again took careful stock of the progress in the only man-in-space program in the United States. And once again, what the Congress saw left them somewhat less than pleased with the facts, prompting a special report to note that, "... a high priority rating does not of itself guarantee that funds, resources, and program approach will represent a maximum effort to attain success at the earliest date."

One aspect more disturbing than others to those officials responsible for financing our manned space effort was the complete absence of a backup program to Mercury. It was noted that the country had already suffered an inexcusable delay by "... an inability to settle the question of management jurisdiction. The program as ultimately approved in October 1958 was virtually the same one already proposed by the Department of Defense in May 1958."

We were risking a disastrous failure in not providing another program that would develop a manned spacecraft system other than the ballistic capsule of Mercury. The Congress severely questioned "whether the national interest is best served by a single approach to this problem." It was, of course, the familiar and dangerous concept of "all the eggs in one basket." The only leeway provided to Mercury was to assure backup contracts on those components for the Mercury system which promised to provide the most extensive trouble. Another program would have added to the costs, but at this stage of the game the costs seemed least important of all the factors involved. The Congress noted that there—

> . . . are a number of very promising alternative approaches to putting man in space. By setting a limit on testing these concepts through exclusive adoption of the Mercury approach, the Nation is risking the loss of extremely valuable development time. The country cannot support a large number of approaches in competition with all the other demands on fiscal and personnel resources. But at the same time the failure to develop in parallel at least one other man-in-space program could prove to be a costly mistake.

The rest is history. Gagarin was in orbit ten months before Glenn left the earth. Titov orbited the planet seventeen times in a 10,000-pound spaceship in August of 1961. If our present plans hold out, we will be able to orbit the earth eighteen times in the summer of 1963, in a 3,000-pound spaceship.

Nikolayev and Popovich performed a dual manned orbital mission in August of 1962. If our present plans hold out—and they are slipping badly—we may attempt a rendezvous with a much smaller and lighter manned spaceship and an unmanned satellite in 1965.

By the time we accomplish our first rendezvous mission, it is likely that the Soviets will (1) have carried out several flights of two or more men in a single spaceship, (2) performed orbital rendezvous and docking, (3) established their first manned station in orbit, and (4) completed their first manned flight around the moon with successful return to the earth.

In our scramble for excuses in the competition in manned space programs, we have turned to every possible source of balm. And one of these has been the repeated statement that the Russians can move faster than we in manned space flight, because they don't care about human lives.

This, of course, led to the conclusion—and more than one high Government official "leaked" this conclusion as fact—that before Yuri Gagarin went into orbit, the Soviets had already stacked up like cordwood the bodies of many cosmonauts who ventured forth into space unsuccessfully.

This issue is old, weary, and ridiculous. Yet the fable persists that the Russians are willing to risk the lives of their men, while we in turn lavish excruciating pains to prevent any disasters in our manned space efforts. It is simply not true. It is certainly true that we have taken nothing for granted, and that to the absolute best of our ability we have placed the safety and the lives of our men above all else. What is completely untrue, however, is the belief that (1) the Russians are callous about the lives of their men, and (2) that our precautions are far more effective than those of the Soviets.

The Russian precautions and preparations are far more extensive than our own, and if anyone enjoys a greater margin of safety during a space mission he is a cosmonaut and not an astronaut. We would much prefer that this situation were not true. But it is, and there has been precious little to do about it. It is the old thorn in the side of our space program; the lack of really big and powerful rocket boosters.

In 1959, Dr. Hugh Dryden, Associate Administrator of NASA, discussed the matter of manned space flight and cautioned: "We must recognize that we may lose the psychological battle to be first. We cannot place prestige above life. A fundamental concept of Project Mercury is that the safe return of the astronaut must be assured. Other nations having less regard for human life may shortcut the development procedures that we think essential and may thereby accomplish manned space flight before we do."

One may reasonably assume that "other nations" refers to the USSR, since this is the only other nation in the world engaged in manned space flight. The word that stands out as strongest in Dr. Dryden's statement is "shortcut."

Astronaut John Glenn orbited the earth three times on February 20, 1962. Before that NASA attempted to send three capsules into orbit in order to verify the entire booster, capsule, re-entry, and recovery systems.

MA-3 (Mercury-Atlas 3) never reached the stratosphere. The Atlas booster disappeared in a crashing explosion of flames. The rocket had not failed but its black boxes had. When the booster did not follow the flight course established for it within its electronic memory units, the Range Safety Officer at Cape Canaveral had no choice but to deliberately destroy the great rocket.

In retrospect, however, this was one of those times when a complete failure becomes a great success. When the rocket was destroyed, the emergency abort system of the Atlas and the capsule worked perfectly. The capsule erupted upward from the Atlas. We caught first sight of the spacecraft as it drifted from behind the dirty gray smear, hanging in the skies, that had once been a beautiful rocket. But for the men who had to ride that "bodacious afterburner," as they call the Atlas, the vindication of that escape system was good cause for sound sleep. Had a man been aboard, he would have been returned to us safely.

Nevertheless, the orbital attempt failed. Several months later, in a repeat of this experiment, we succeeded in sending an unmanned capsule on a single orbit of the earth. The entire mission came off with flying colors. After another period of several months passed, we were ready for a complete dress rehearsal of the manned flight. Carrying the chimpanzee Enos, MA-5 rocketed upward from Cape Canaveral and was injected successfully into orbit.

The mission called for three full orbits of the earth, but we failed to complete this requirement. When the electrical power system of the capsule acted in an erratic fashion, Mercury Control cut short the flight after two full orbits. We then declared the systems ready for the first manned flight.

So before Glenn's mission there were three orbital attempts— with one failure and two successes. One mission lasted one orbit, the second mission was a 95 percent success, even though the flight ended after two orbits rather than three. The total came to two missions flown with three orbits in all.

The Soviets placed five unmanned spacecraft in orbit. They were successful in all five attempts. They attempted to recover all five spaceships and failed in two of these missions.

Spacecraft I orbited the earth for several days prior to the re-entry attempt. The attitude stabilization system failed to position the spacecraft properly; the retrorockets, instead of decelerating the ship, kicked it into a higher orbit.

Spacecraft II, with two dogs, forty animals, and extensive bio-medical research equipment, orbited the earth seventeen times. Recovery was successful.

Spacecraft III orbited the earth an estimated seventeen times. Upon attempted recovery the attitude control system malfunctioned. Instead of decelerating and entering the atmosphere, the spacecraft drove into the atmosphere at high speed and at an undesired angle. It burned on re-entry.

Spacecraft IV orbited the earth an estimated six times, on March 9, 1961. Recovery was perfect. Sixteen days later Spacecraft V orbited the earth an estimated six times. Recovery was perfect.

Eighteen days later Yuri Gagarin went into orbit.

The final result showed five successful orbits out of five attempts, and three successful recoveries out of the five ships orbited. Apparently the Russians considered their problems solved, as they fired Spacecraft IV and V in rapid succession, and followed quickly with Gagarin's mission.

Our two orbital missions for a total of three orbits may hardly be said to represent an overwhelming superiority in preparations, when compared to the five successful orbital missions, the three recoveries, and several dozens of orbits by the Russians.

But this is only part of the picture. To understand the advantages in the Russian spacecraft system, we must compare the Mercury and Vostok vehicles. Both the Mercury and Vostok spacecraft have escape rocket systems and parachute recovery systems. The comparison ends there. During powered ascent, the Russian has two emergency escape systems. He can use the Vostok escape rockets, or he can blast himself free on a powerful ejection seat from the spaceship itself. He may elect to ride the Vostok away from the booster, and then eject to descend beneath his own parachute.

The Mercury capsule does not have an ejection seat system. The Mercury astronaut doesn't even have a parachute. There's no use in supplying one (as we did for the Shepard flight). The astronaut couldn't get out of the capsule even if he wanted to. It is too small and cramped, and the escape hatch is too confined in a high airblast during uncontrolled descent to permit escape.

During the descent through the atmosphere after re-entry, if the Mercury parachute system fails we will need an astronaut replacement. The parachute system is the only landing system of the capsule. During the Vostok descent through the atmosphere after re-entry, if the parachute system fails, the cosmonaut can eject himself from the spacecraft (as did Titov, Nikolayev, and Popovich, but not Gagarin), and descend beneath his own parachute.

One of the key pacing factors for any space program is the availability of launch facilities.

The Mercury program has only one launch pad at Cape Canaveral that can accommodate the Mercury-Atlas system. It is for this reason, as much as any other, that we have always had to wait several months from one astronaut flight to the other. The Russians, on the other hand, employ a series of launch pads. In 1961 they fired three Vostoks, two unmanned and one manned, within a period of one month. In 1962 they fired two manned Vostoks within a period of 24 hours.

More pertinent to the matter of time is the danger in using only one pad. If the rocket explodes while it is on the pad, and many a rocket has done exactly that, then the launch pad facilities may be knocked out of commission for a period of two to six months. It has never been possible to place two boosters on two separate pads at the same time so that in the event of malfunction or difficulty with one vehicle, the other could be used almost immediately as a backup.

In respect to "a sense of urgency," no further comment is necessary.

The organization of spacemen, astronauts and cosmonauts, is a tightly knit fraternity. There are few members, and only a slightly larger number of potential applicants. The task of training an astronaut is long, arduous, and terribly expensive. The process of an astronaut in gaining orbital experience is longer, even more arduous, far more expensive, and it is also dangerous. Since experience is so difficult to come by and so rare, it is an essential ingredient in any space program. As our activities in space are projected for not only years but decades, the first astronauts play the most vital role in the program.

The Russians have selected their men carefully, just as our selection has been exceedingly demanding. The Russians specified youth as a part of their selection program. They intend, as they have emphasized, to utilize their cosmonauts for long periods of time, to capitalize on their invaluable experience for future activities in space. The United States has decided otherwise. The policy of our federal space agency is that the astronauts are to be on duty as astronauts only as a temporary expedient. The official policy is that after their extensive training, they will be allowed to accumulate only limited experience *and will then be removed from the program.*

In March of 1960, Dr. T. Keith Glennan, then the NASA Administrator, was queried by a member of the House Committee on Science and Astronautics, "Why don't you have each of the astronauts separated from his service so there will be no competition among the Navy, the Air Force, and the Marines . . . Why shouldn't these people be civilians during the time they are working with your agency, NASA, and then later if they want to return to the military services, all right? I think it would be much better if they are treated as scientists and explorers rather than as Navy, Air Force, or Marine Corps personnel."

To this question, Dr. Glennan replied that "The reason for not transferring these men directly to NASA as against assigning them to us, where they now operate as civilians is simply that they will probably go back to their services. That is their career. The act of separating them from their service and making them civilians for *these two or three years* [emphasis added: MC], seems really an unnecessary action."

CHAPTER **15.**

A MILLION MILES TO THE MOON

IN the spring of 1961, in a blaze of imminent glory, the United States shook off the doldrums of previous years and announced its commitment to, in the words of the President, "a great new American enterprise." In short—we were going to the moon. We had all along, but in a half-hearted and nebulous way, always assumed this was to be one of the destinations of our national space effort. We didn't quite know when, or how. We just knew that we were going. The National Astronautics and Space Administration had muttered something about 1971 to 1975, but even this seemed unlikely.

The President wasn't pleased with this schedule, which wasn't really a schedule after all. He stated that we were going to have an American walking on the surface of the moon "before the decade is out." There were cries of consternation among those responsible for seeing this Presidential commitment through to its realization. And in the spring of 1961, this presented some problems: namely, how were we going to do it?

Six months later, indecision still reigned. In the struggle to discern how we were going to the moon, a plaintive remark, which, in Washington has become a catch-all for official misery, was heard: "Who's in charge here?"

Another year and more has passed since the fall and winter of 1961. In this interim something happened in the American space program that still leaves one breathless.

We made the decision on how we were to go to the moon. And then we changed our minds.

We re-evaluated all the aspects of the situation, and announced cheerfully that finally we had worked out all the problems. Our choice was for EOR—Earth Orbital Rendezvous. We would build huge rocket launch vehicles, standing nearly four hundred feet tall and weighing more than six million pounds each. We would fire two of these monsters into orbit about the earth, and we would fire them with such superb precision that they would rendezvous as they swept around the planet. There, in free fall, our spacemen-engineers-mechanics would shove and pull and push until two huge ships were joined as one. The men would then wriggle back into their command capsules, batten down the hatches, and blast off from earth orbit toward the moon. The grand finale to this massive production would be the sight of a 150,000-pound spaceship, five stories tall, descending on a pillar of gleaming fire to the surface of the moon.

And that was how we were going to the moon. For a few months, anyway.

Some of the scientists soon discovered they were sleeping fitfully at night. They came to work with worried frowns on their faces. They jiggled slide-rules and scribbled notes, and then they met in large rooms, locked the doors, and shouted at one another. Finally they opened the doors, and made an announcement. EOR wasn't very good, after all. In fact, there were so many misgivings about EOR and that 150,000-pound spaceship, that NASA had decided to scrap the whole idea and go off on a new tangent.

This time the "how" involved the oddities of LOR and LEM, which may be identified as Lunar Orbital Rendezvous, and Lunar Excursion Module. LOR retained that monster launching vehicle of 6,000,000 pounds and a first-stage thrust of 7,500,000 pounds.

But there would be no more rendezvous around the earth. The scientists had figured out a trickier way to get to the moon.

Under the new program, a Saturn V would leave Cape Canaveral and orbit the earth. The remaining assembly of the spaceship in orbit would make a swing of at least one-half this planet, while computers clicked and the three astronauts aboard cinched their safety belts just a bit tighter. When everything fell into its proper place, the astronauts would ignite the motors of the rocket stage to which they were still attached. The spaceship assembly would then whip outward from its orbit. When the assembly reached a speed of 25,000 miles per hour, power would be cut. The assembly—known as Apollo—would at that time be falling toward the moon.

At this moment some very intricate and tricky maneuvers must be carried out. At the front end of the Apollo spaceship system is a squat cone-shaped object known as the Command Module. Here the astronauts make their home in space. Behind the Command Module is a bulky Service Module, crammed with fuel tanks, a rocket engine and power packs. Behind the Service Module, its legs squeezed together like a crab, is LEM, the Lunar Excursion Module. This unlovely mechanical creature, known immediately to all concerned as the *Bug,* has to be shifted from its position of trailing the Service Module to a new position where it can be mated nose-to-nose with the Command Module.

In this fashion the whole conglomeration, weighing 85,000 pounds, would continue in its curving drift toward the moon. The astronauts, understandably concerned for their safety and well-being, would maintain constant touch with the earth. They would, several times during their journey, make slight adjustments of their moonbound drift by squeezing out bursts of fire from their rockets.

Finally, if all goes well (the luck chant of Canaveral), the jumble of spacecraft objects swings toward the moon. The astronauts then ripple off some bursts of fire from their rocket engines, and settle down in a nice, comfortable orbit about one hundred miles above the moon.

From this point this simplified version of our moon program becomes a bit difficult to handle. Two of the astronauts bid farewell to the man who will remain in lunar orbit aboard the squat cone of Apollo. Of course, if in the process of attempting to land on, and leave from, the lunar surface something should go awry there will always be that one man still around, so that he at least can return to earth.

After saying goodbye, the two astronauts crawl through an airlock into their ungainly Bug. They cast off from the Apollo, fire a blast of power, and settle down into a new orbit. This is a looping curve that brings them down to within ten miles of the lunar surface, so that they may make a choice of the best landing site.

Now come the fanciest maneuvers of this whole operation. Having selected their site, the astronauts fire reaction jets to place the Bug in exactly the attitude desired. Then they fire off another blast with their main propulsion system, to decelerate. The Bug falls toward the moon. Since the moon is an airless world, there is not even the comfortable tug of air resistance or a welcoming scream of air past the metal skin. There is not even, contrary to science fiction, the blessed silence of space. The two astronauts will hear the sound of their breathing magnified in their microphone-to-headset systems, the thumping of air pressurization equipment, the grinding of dozens of other pieces of equipment, the vibration and shuddering roar of their rockets, the pounding of their hearts and—who knows?—perhaps some shouted words of encouragement from their fellow left behind in lunar orbit.

Another long blast of power and, it is to be hoped, an extremely precise balance of rocket thrust with the weight of the unlovely spaceship. Now begins a translational maneuver. The Bug carries enough fuel to permit exactly sixty seconds of hovering or moving a thousand feet in any direction before settling on the moon's surface.

The final maneuver is to ease the Bug on its spindly legs to the surface—with a fervent prayer that (1) the impact is gentle, (2) the Bug doesn't topple over, and (3) that the Bug does not sink out of sight into what may be a deep sea of dust on the moon.

The brief stay on the moon, anywhere from a few hours to four days is as specific as NASA would be, will not be without its moments of awe, beauty, and constant, unremitting danger. The two men must never for an instant forget they are in a savage and merciless environment. A single slip, one mistake in total vacuum, and the story is ended. On the airless moon, they will be subjected at any moment to a meteor strike and a tiny pebble slamming into the Bug can be quite disastrous.

Assuming that none of these unpleasantries came to pass, the astronauts, after scientific research on the moon, would prepare for their return. This involves a complete and meticulous checkout of the Bug and its systems. Then, coordinating their every move with the Apollo still in orbit, the upper half of the Bug blasts free of the moon, leaving the spindly legs and base of the vehicle behind. With continued good fortune, the Bug arcs up through vacuum in a long swooping ascent, and slides neatly into formation, at the same height, velocity, plane, and orbital inclination as the waiting Apollo. The astronauts must then transfer themselves and their bottled samples of moondust from the Bug to the Command Module. With everything secure, they kick against the Bug to cast it free, fire up their engines, and begin the long return to earth.

The trip back to earth must be performed with exquisite accuracy so that the three astronauts do not miss the earth and go sailing out into space. They must return along exacting trajectories, their every movement calculated down to the last fraction of a second and *nth* of a degree. After all this transpires, their reward is a shrieking, blazing plunge through the atmosphere at 25,000 miles per hour, a scene resplendent with shock waves ahead of the Apollo reaching perhaps 15,000 degrees in temperature, to say nothing of the several thousands of degrees generated against the heat shield of the spaceship proper.

The journey reaches its anticlimatic end with the popping of three great parachutes, and a swaying descent to the earth much in the same manner of ancient aeronauts.

That is the schedule and the list of events for Project Apollo— our mission to the moon. There is, perhaps, one unexpected bright ray of hope in all this. As one engineer remarked with a strange look upon his face, "If the boys get into trouble, they can always ask for help. From the Russians, of course."

There are many keys to the vaults of space, but the one that opens the door widest is the key of propulsion. Power is the cornerstone on which a space program is built—power for satellites, manned spacecraft and, above all, power in Niagara-like quantities for the ships that will sail to the moon. The record of the United States in this area leaves more than a little to be desired. An energetic program has been under way now for several years to overcome our weaknesses in this matter, but the direction of the program has unfortunately not been of the strongest. There is nothing lacking in the engineering and scientific capabilities of industry to produce all the power this country requires—and more. There is a great deal lacking in guiding and sustaining the programs to make that propulsion energy available.

Two years after the first Russian satellites went into orbit—two years after this country allegedly embarked on a hard-driving program to make up for wasted time—the Congress reviewed where we stood in propulsion.* The facts did not engender confidence:

> Propulsion is the key to space travel. Although many technical elements must be combined to build a successful space ship, without propulsion they are nothing. . . . the key role of

* "Space Propulsion," Report No. 26; August 31, 1959; House Committee on Science and Astronautics.

propulsion is illustrated by the frustration the United States has felt in the last two years. We have had a capacity to build a host of beautifully miniaturized instruments and devices, and have shown a broad capability to meet the challenges of a new technological age. Yet most of our satellites have been compared with grapefruit, and could do only so much. In contrast, whether or not the Soviet Union made the most of its opportunity, it did at least have the opportunity to put even thousands of pounds of payload into Earth orbit. For a solar orbit, the 13.4 pounds of our Pioneer IV greatly limited our opportunities, as contrasted with the reported 796 pounds of instruments, or 3,245 pounds of orbiting body of the Soviet Mechta [Lunik].

. . . the problems of space propulsion now are being vigorously attacked in many respects. In retrospect, some of these efforts began too late and, even now, some of the problems are so vaguely defined that we do not realize how much effort is required for solution. It is possible, then, that such problems may not be getting the kind of attention they deserve and require.

It is now obvious to all that had we instituted a strong program for development of large rocket engines at the close of World War II when we had great but untapped capabilities, we would not now be in a position of second place to the USSR so far as "weightlifting" capability is concerned. But this is past, and now we must do our best to make up for lost time. . . .

The truth of the matter is that, despite the obvious overwhelming superiority of the USSR in great boosters, a superiority attested to by Soviet deeds and our own admissions, the American program to regain stature as a major space power has been torn by gross inefficiency, indecision, inability to understand the problems involved or to discover their solutions, and, above all, by an astonishing lack of urgency.

Our booster program has been lethargic. Throughout the entire process of booster development there has been a strange aversion to getting the job done just as quickly as it might be accomplished even within the bounds of granted authority and appropriated funds. It is one thing to acknowledge our lack of foresight and even the scientific hostility to space programs before the future became so obvious. But the continuation of our refusal to accept the obvious can only mean chaotic inefficiency within the organizations responsible for getting us back into the race.

Almost one year before the Congress created NASA, the Air Force studied an exhaustive proposal from the General Dynamics/ Astronautics Corporation to develop a new space booster vehicle that could give the United States in the shortest possible time a means of orbiting heavy payloads. That vehicle was the Atlas-Centaur, or Centaur for short.

It involved using the Atlas ICBM as a first-stage booster, thereby saving many millions of dollars and years of development time for this particular vehicle. The second stage of the rocket would be a new propulsion system, utilizing for the first time in this country the high-energy fuel, liquid-hydrogen. Mixed with liquid-oxygen, this new fuel afforded the promise of boosting into earth orbit payloads as great as 8,500 pounds; sending payloads of 2,500 pounds to the moon; and launching payloads as great as 1,500 pounds to Mars and Venus.

By August of 1958, ARPA accepted from the Air Force a more elaborate proposal for the Centaur and assigned authority for the development program to the Air Force. Centaur promised new muscle in space. In 1958, when the development program went into the official hopper as a hardware item, the heaviest Russian satellite orbiting the earth was the 3,000-pound Sputnik III.

We planned the first Centaur flight for January of 1961, and operational missions before that year was out. Centaur payloads of 8,500 pounds would compare favorably to the 10,400 pounds of the Vostoks, and at least give us a fighting chance with the

14,100 pounds of Sputniks VII and VIII, launched in February of 1961, if the program had proceeded according to plan. Unfortunately the program did not proceed according to plan. Indeed, it began to fall apart at the seams.

It would be difficult to over-emphasize the critical role we assigned to Centaur in our long-range space effort. This was not to be just another booster, but *the* booster rocket by which we would conduct extensive earth orbit missions, lunar investigations, and planetary studies. Aside from the military satellite missions assigned to Centaur, which were considerable, NASA alone planned to launch one operational Centaur every month for a period extending well into 1970 or later. The failure of the Centaur program has struck severely at our national space effort, and it has not only badly crippled some projects; it has also forced cancellation of others.

We counted on Centaur to fill the wide performance gap between Atlas-Agena and Saturn. That represents an orbital payload gap of from 3,000 pounds to 20,000 pounds. Planned for 8,500-pound orbital payloads, Centaur promised a bonanza of mission returns. This was only the surface value of the program. Even more critical to our space mission capabilities was the development of Centaur's upper-stage liquid-hydrogen engine system.

This is vital to anyone interested in where America is going in space. Congress explained that fact in this statement:

> . . . virtually all upper stages of large future space vehicles, both chemical and nuclear, are presently intended to utilize hydrogen as fuel. Thus, the Centaur vehicle is actually a research and development tool. It is intended to provide the essential experience in handling, storing, and using liquid hydrogen, solve the many associated problems, and furnish the techniques and components required to harness for operational use this high energy fuel, for which there appears no readily applicable substitute. In short, Centaur is performing

a technical pioneering function which is considered vital to the future of much of the nation's space effort.

Some basic comparisons will stress the critical role of the liquid-hydrogen propulsion system. Using the standard fuel combination of kerosene and liquid-oxygen, a booster can orbit a payload of 1,000 pounds. By shifting to a liquid-hydrogen upper stage, without adding any weight to the vehicle, the payload jumps to 1,400 pounds. There is a free dividend of 400 pounds—or 40 percent of any orbital mission about the earth.

This constitutes only the beginning of the remarkable gains inherent in the liquid-hydrogen system. If we wish to send a payload to the moon, the free dividend leaps to 90 percent. When the rocket capable of firing a 1,000-pound payload to the moon shifts to a liquid-hydrogen upper stage, it suddenly is capable of increasing that same payload to 1,900 pounds. And, states Colonel Donald H. Heaton, former Director of Vehicles, Office of Space Sciences, NASA, for the still-higher-velocity Venus mission, "the payload increase attributable to high energy propellants rises still further to at least 100 percent—that is, double the payload which a similar size vehicle using only propellants of conventional energy could carry."

In the summer of 1962, NASA planned a Mariner spacecraft mission to Venus with a payload of 1,450 pounds. Centaur was not available, so the payload boosted with the Atlas-Agena B dropped to well under 500 pounds. In November of 1962, NASA planned a Mariner spacecraft mission to Mars. Because of the positions of the two planets, the payload would have to be reduced to less than 600 pounds. Centaur was not available; Atlas-Agena B at this time could boost a payload to Mars of only 200 pounds. Virtually no instrument could be carried. NASA canceled the Mars spacecraft mission.

The Russians fired a probe to Mars weighing 1,965 pounds—under the "worst possible" launch conditions. Under optimum conditions, with Mars and Earth in a position reducing the performance requirements, engineers estimate that the payload of the same Russian booster that kicked Mars I into its interplanetary orbit could be increased to about two and a half tons. In the meantime our next schedule for a Mars shoot would not come before late 1964. Because Centaur is not available there will be no shot to Mars until that time, and perhaps not until 1966 or 1967.

During June of 1962, Colonel Heaton had in no uncertain terms warned of the danger that such cancellations might be necessary when he explained that: "It is abundantly evident that the penalty for failing to learn how to harness the high energy of hydrogen effectively, reliably, and promptly would prove exceedingly costly in money and time."

In a mood of deep concern, the Congress warned that: "Many proposed larger, more sophisticated launch vehicles will be possible only after Centaur has solved the numerous problems associated with the use of hydrogen fuel."

ARPA scheduled the first Centaur flight test for January of 1961, more than two years after the contract for Centaur development went to General Dynamics/Astronautics. For the six months afterward, the flight schedule called for a launching every thirty days.

The schedule was hopelessly overoptimistic.

On July 1, 1959, NASA took over jurisdiction for Centaur from the Department of Defense. In order to maintain continuity in the development effort, NASA retained the Air Force project manager. Six months later, Centaur assumed an expanded and even more critical role. NASA canceled its projected Vega booster vehicle, and the mission responsibilities previously assigned to Vega went to Centaur. At about this same time the decision was made to utilize Centaur as the booster vehicle for Advent, a vital military communications satellite to be placed in orbit at 22,300 miles above the earth, and also for the Mariner and Surveyor spacecraft for the decade-long NASA lunar and planetary exploration programs.

By the summer of 1960, NASA concluded that the six vehicles to be used in flight testing would be inadequate to meet mission development needs. The program expanded to ten flight test vehicles—"An absolute minimum to prove out a vehicle design upon which so much of the national space program was beginning to depend." Centaur's importance rose another notch when the Government made its decision to utilize liquid hydrogen as the propellant for our nuclear engines in spacecraft. Then came another decision, casting Centaur as the single most vital instrument in the burgeoning space effort. The Saturn and Nova booster vehicles also would use the high-energy hydrogen fuel. Centaur became the focal point on which would pivot the ultimate success or failure of long-range space programs, both unmanned and manned.

But in the winter of 1959–60 the delays began to crop up. They appeared first as a trickle, and then the trickle became an avalanche of problems, failures, test-stand explosions, and other delays which have completely thrown out all the early hopes for Centaur.

The most critical problem that directly forced delays in the flight test schedule was not that of engineering but of money. NASA made the decision that the funds needed for Centaur were more urgently needed elsewhere and Pratt & Whitney, producers of the upper-stage engines, reluctantly rescheduled its development program. The flight schedule slipped from January to June of 1961. The previous optimism for Centaur already was dissipating in terms of development time, and instead of one flight test every month, NASA instead doubled the time between firings.

A series of explosions in test-stand ignitions of the Centaur engines made it painfully clear that even June of 1961 would be a hopelessly premature date for the first flight test. Pratt & Whitney had completed 230 successful engine ignitions, when three disastrous explosions shook the entire development schedule. After identifying and correcting the cause of its troubles, Pratt & Whitney then performed more than 700 successful firings of the Centaur engines without a single failure.

Trouble cropped up in other areas. The delay in engine development affected engine delivery schedules. The engines with their new ignition systems could not be delivered to NASA until June of 1961, which meant another change in the scheduled firing date, to November. At Cape Canaveral mechanical, weather, electronic, and engineering difficulties plagued the launch-ready crews. The flight test date slipped once again to December.

Centaur had become the focal point, it seemed, for a torrent of development programs. Week after week the difficulties with both the vehicle and its launch complex continued to harass the engineers and the launch date slipped another four months. On May 8, 1962, the first Centaur rose from its pad. It was a perfect launch with the familiar cascade of brilliant flames from the Atlas thundering back. Fifty-four seconds after launch, with the first-stage booster functioning perfectly, the Centaur upper stage exploded.

One month later the Department of Defense announced that the entire Advent satellite program had undergone a "major reorientation" in order "to bring it into consonance with available boosters." The problems were complex, but they also underscored that the planned payload capability had proved overly optimistic in the development of Centaur. The Advent satellite increased slightly in weight, but what really counted was that Centaur's orbital payload capacity had slipped in the other direction.

DOD officials took little pains to conceal their opinions that they considered the entire scope of the Centaur program as impossibly optimistic and also said that they were convinced that: "Operational Centaur launch vehicles will not be available until 1966, two years later than Advent was originally scheduled to go into limited operational use."

The Congress wrote a partial epitaph to Centaur when it noted (July 2, 1962) that: "Virtually all aspects of these two development programs seem to have combined to make continuation of Advent a poor investment, and to force cancellation of a program on which the Department of Defense has already spent over $170 million. From the standpoint of Centaur, one of its major missions no longer exists."

NASA scheduled the second flight test of Centaur for October of 1962. Again the schedule proved unduly optimistic, and October came and went without a flight. A third flight had been scheduled for the end of 1962 but this even higher hope vanished.

The second Centaur scheduled for a flight test launching was installed on a static test stand in Sycamore Canyon, California, for exhaustive checkout. On a nearby stand was an Atlas-F ICBM. During an engine run, the Atlas-F exploded. The force of the explosion ripped through the area with such intensity that it subjected the Centaur to excessive overpressure. Dismayed engineers stared at the damaged Centaur. Sadly, they moved the next scheduled firing date well into 1963.

What's the story behind this succession of failures, delays, and even mission cancellations in a program of "key significance" to our national space effort—a fact that the Congress acidly noted "was not just discovered," but had "been known for a long time"?

Aside from the technical and engineering difficulties, which contributed only a minor part to the extensive delays: ". . . the Centaur development program appears to have been a low-pressure effort during its entire history. From all appearances, General Dynamics/Astronautics, the prime contractor, has been preoccupied with the Atlas ICBM program, and resisted, until quite recently, making any really significant changes in its management of the Centaur program, despite repeated urging by NASA officials to adopt management changes at an earlier date."

NASA officials spared no effort to place the blame squarely on General Dynamics/Astronautics. They accused the firm of curtailing its test programs "to a hardly defendable extent" because of financial shortages. The curtailment of these tests, in turn, permitted integrating Centaur components and assemblies into the final vehicle prematurely—and NASA acidly commented that proper management could "have saved a lot of money, delays, and embarrassment . . ."

But was NASA using General Dynamics/Astronautics as a scapegoat to avoid its own share of blame? The Congress noted: "Management on the part of the Government also appears . . . to have been inadequate."

There could be little argument about this matter. The surveillance of all technical aspects of the Centaur program in the joint Air Force-NASA management effort was carried out by a group of only eight people including "secretarial and clerical personnel." Eventually this grew to fifteen people, again including "secretarial and clerical personnel."

Dr. Wernher von Braun noted with some misgivings that a staff of such limited size was simply "inadequate coverage on the part of the Government," especially in "a program of this magnitude, involving engine development going on in Florida, and vehicle development in southern California." How long did this "admittedly inadequate technical supervision" continue? In 1962 the problem still existed—and its solution had not yet been applied. By the summer of 1962, NASA had still not requested a DX priority for Centaur.

The conclusion of the Congressional Subcommittee that investigated the Centaur program was:

> . . . management of the Centaur development program has been weak and ineffective both at NASA headquarters and in the field, and . . . the program has suffered from a diffusion of authority and responsibility.
> . . . proper evaluation of the importance of the Centaur launch vehicle might well have resulted in requests for additional funds in the past, in order to support a funding level commensurate with the importance of the development program. Not only might delays in the program have been avoided

by adequate funding, but certain additional expenses and outright losses might not have been incurred. The facts remain
that additional funds were not requested, costs have risen,
and losses have been incurred.

... In view of Centaur's key role in the Nation's space
effort, [it is] difficult to understand the apparent low priority
status of the development program since its inception.

By the beginning of 1963 the lag in the Centaur program had
reduced payload of lunar exploratory vehicles; reduced payload of
future lunar vehicles resulting in extensive redesign and cutback in
anticipated payloads; reduced payloads in Venus spacecraft; canceled the Advent satellite in 22,300-mile orbit; and canceled the
1962 Mars spacecraft missions. By the spring of 1963, one flight
had been made, in May of 1962, which exploded 54 seconds after
launch.

The most efficient rocket engine burning chemical fuels is an
inefficient monster. It is a fuel-gulping creature with an appetite so
voracious as to strain credulity. In just sixty seconds a current
rocket booster drains more fuel than a heavy jetliner consumes on
a transcontinental flight. Most of the bulk and weight of the rocket
boosters are made up of huge fuel tanks and ponderous fuel loads.
And no matter what heights of efficiency and engineering skill we
may climb with the chemical rocket, there's no evading the fact
that we're still working with a clumsy, dangerous, volatile dinosaur.

There's little we can do about this problem—at the moment.
We have no choice but to use these huge and clumsy brutes to
fight the massive pull of earth's gravity. And it is obvious to any
engineer that the road leads only to a dead end. Just as we rid
ourselves of the steam engine and the propeller to make room for
radical new innovations in power, so we must as quickly as possible get away from our dependence upon the chemical rockets.

The next step toward attaining a true power capability for space
lies in nuclear propulsion. It is unbelievably more efficient and it
is much more satisfactory to use. We need more power, velocities

far higher than those we deal with today, and above all we need vehicle maneuverability and mission flexibility. In terms of long-range programs connected with the moon, and scientific expeditions placed on the other planets, we are going about our space business in antiquated Model-T rockets. It is not good enough. We've got to tap the atom. Only then are we going to gain some desperately needed freedom in space missions and end our days of slavery to the crude arks within which we stagger into space.

The United States effort to gain nuclear propulsion capability is Project Rover, a venture initiated in 1955 under the joint auspices of the U.S. Air Force and the Atomic Energy Commission. From the inception of the program, responsibility was divided clearly into two areas. The AEC's Los Alamos Scientific Laboratory in New Mexico attended to the development of the actual research reactors, and to the testing and feasibility demonstrations of the heart of the propulsion systems. Simultaneously with this work, the Air Force hammered at the knotty problems of developing the nonnuclear engine and vehicle components.

The more scientists studied the potentialities of Rover (and the family of nuclear drive vehicles which were to follow this initial effort) the brighter the future loomed for its true capabilities in space, despite problems of heavy shielding for the crew. The largest and most efficient chemical rocket because of its inherent energy limitations could not hope to compete with even a relatively inefficient nuclear engine system.

The "free wheeling" of the nuclear propulsion package becomes especially evident as the mission increases in its demands and the vehicle expands in size. As the weight of the payload increases, and the distance to cover soars, and the velocity requirements shoot up, the nuclear rocket comes into its own. The greater the requirements the more efficient and economical the nuclear drive rocket. It is a development curve that delights engineers. What is most important is that the rate of increase of fuel for the nuclear rocket for higher performances is much less than the rate of increase for the chemical rocket. Finally there is a point where, as the mission becomes more difficult, the nuclear rocket becomes smaller, lighter, and cheaper than the best of all chemical rockets.

There's yet another and most vital dividend. This is the matter of reliability. With the greatly increased power of the nuclear system, it becomes possible to reduce the number of rocket stages for a particular mission. And the staging processes increase the potential of failure for a space shot tremendously. It is necessary to have a perfect cutoff operation of the bottom stage. Timers and relays must function within a rigid time sequence. A wide gamut of operations must occur; pressurization buildup, electrical energy flow, explosive bolt operation, separation of interfaces, adjustment of guidance systems, ignition under vacuum conditions, and so on. Each of these operations is a potential bit of disaster and many a space mission that started out perfectly has gone down the drain when some minor failure in the final stage occurred. One of our lunar probes, successful for 99 percent of the entire mission up to that moment, failed when a small piece of wire snapped.

Whatever complexity we have known before will be simplicity itself compared to the new behemoths under accelerated development. The Thor-Able rocket, for example, has three stages but also dozens of intricate operations to perform through the propulsion part of any flight. Each booster has but one main engine, and yet the complications of any operation using three different rocket stages demand the most sensitive care and preparation.

The new boosters stagger the imagination. The Saturn I has eight huge engines in its first stage. Shutdown of this stage in flight requires an intricate series of operations, the firing of explosive bolts and a number of small separation rockets. And when all this is completed, the S-IV upper stage of this vehicle must then ignite. And that means simultaneous (down to hundredths of a second) ignition of six liquid-hydrogen engines under space conditions. On a planetary mission, the same shutdown and separation process as occurred earlier in the flight must be repeated. When S-IV shuts down, the S-V stage, with two more liquid-hydrogen engines, must fire. So we have, for this single mission, the step-process of igniting a total of sixteen engines in three separate, intricate processes.

The rule-of-thumb for such operations is that the reliability of multistage vehicles declines sharply in direct proportion to the number of engines and the number of stages. With the nuclear rocket it may be possible to eliminate staging operations on certain types of missions. Or at the least, the intricacies of staging and engine operation will be greatly reduced and reliability increased proportionally.

Above all, there are certain types of missions which appear to lie beyond the capabilities of chemical rocket systems. If we are to engage freely in the missions we feel essential to a true and sound program, especially on manned interplanetary ones, the nuclear rocket is indispensable. The goals on the nuclear drive horizon are dazzling, but they are not without their thorny problems. Nuclear propulsion systems demand much of engineers in perfecting materials which will operate under extreme temperatures. The work performed in conventional nuclear reactors does not apply to space drive systems since in the latter the reactor must be brought to its operating temperature of thousands of degrees in a period of seconds. Fortunately, there seems to be a balance even in the face of these serious obstacles. The nuclear rocket does not need to function at full power for years, only for minutes.

After an exhaustive study of the nuclear systems, the Congress concluded: *

> Nuclear enthusiasts admit that very difficult problems must be solved before a nuclear rocket will be a reality, but they contend that these problems do not involve scientific breakthroughs, and that the rewards are great enough to justify a much greater effort. More money will be required for this

* "Project Rover (U.S. Nuclear Rocket Development Program)"; Staff Report of the Committee on Science and Astronautics, House of Representatives Report No. 377, May 9, 1961.

greater effort, of course; but if nuclear propulsion systems become available earlier than now programmed, a great deal of money now scheduled to be spent for huge chemical systems of the late 1960's may be saved. A decision on the relative merits of the nuclear rocket and the so-called Nova chemical rocket someday may have to be made. . . . supporting enormous chemical systems while ignoring nuclear rockets has been described as "flirting with obsolescence," a conclusion with which the committee concurs. Basic policy decisions must be made in the near future, and the 1962 budget may be critical, since it will tend to establish direction and emphasis.

The fundamental question appears to be this: To what extent is the United States willing to commit itself to a man-in-space program? If this Nation is serious about manned space flight and deep space exploration, it is the conviction of the committee that nuclear propulsion must be developed in spite of its high cost, and that Project Rover should be administered in a more dynamic manner than in the past. *A very vigorous program could vault this country's space capability to a position of dominance.* [Emphasis added: MC]

What about nuclear propulsion research before Project Rover? Was there some basis, no matter how slight, which we could use as a starting point? There was ANP—Aircraft Nuclear Propulsion. It had been in existence since 1946. But when officials looked at the record of that program, they shuddered. Senator Clinton P. Anderson on January 16, 1958 took dead aim at this effort:

> . . . in order to press forward vigorously and effectively in developing nuclear rocket propulsion we need a program that has clear objectives, even if they can't be too precise at this stage of the game. We also need clear lines of authority and steady support for the program so that it can be pursued to a successful conclusion at the earliest time.
>
> . . . I hope we don't get into the same fix we have been in for over 10 years with the aircraft nuclear propulsion program. Beginning with the old NEPA project in 1946, the ANP

program has been characterized by ups and downs in funding, by on-again-off-again planning, and by an administrative setup that has been just short of chaotic at times. As far as I can see there never have been any real clear objectives nor have the contractors been able to find out where the program is going from year to year. In 1953 Secretary Wilson attempted to kill the project outright but thanks to the intervention of the Joint Committee on Atomic Energy—and particularly through the efforts of Melvin Price and the late Carl Hinshaw of the other House—it was kept going somehow. After 10 long years of this merry-go-round, it now appears that the project is once again getting back on its feet. But it's been a long and costly wait.

A study of the problems left little conviction that we had accepted the challenge of nuclear rocket propulsion. Until 1958 the military services had performed research activities in trying to develop a nuclear power plant for missiles and space vehicles, but this program was strangled almost from its start by crippling budgetary cutbacks and lack of authority. It was not a program, but an effort marked with sporadic starts and stops and undisguised despair on the part of the technicians most closely associated with the project.

Dr. Norris G. Bradbury, the director of the Los Alamos Scientific Laboratory, was described sympathetically as a man "who has to cook his pot too far back on the stove."

Staffing the Atomic Energy Commission's extensive laboratory and field office facilities were some of the finest scientists and engineers in the world. Their record, Senator Anderson emphasized to the nation, had been that of "men deeply dedicated to the public good." But this same dedication availed these men little in the attempts to get the ball rolling in nuclear propulsion for space missions. The deeper the investigations went, the more damning the evidence became. Operating on the basis of "taking nothing for granted," investigating officials were startled to learn that "less than one percent of all these scientists and engineers have even had the opportunity to study the role of nuclear power as applied to missiles, much less outer space."

Between the time of Sputnik I and May of 1958 not a single Government agency official, or anyone from the executive division of the Government, impressed upon the Atomic Energy Commission the critical need to get a program for the development of nuclear space propulsion into action. The Atomic Energy Commission lacked any "requirements" in their operations "to conduct broad studies on outer space propulsion." Warming to the subject, Senator Anderson clearly accused the President of being "completely silent on atomic power and it may be that little thought has been given to the subject."

What brought the Congressional investigators to the boiling point was the fact that full authority existed, and had existed for some time, to gain momentum in nuclear space propulsion research. The only requirement was an administrative order and nothing else. The funds necessary to initiate this effort were identified as being "moderate" because, as it was emphasized, "all the facilities exist and the people are already employed. There would be no expenditures for components or hardware—only for study time."

In 1958, NASA assumed the Air Force's responsibilities in the joint Air Force-AEC development of the Project Rover program to produce a nuclear spaceship drive. NASA's inheritance wasn't much to cheer about. Long before NASA entered the picture, the Department of Defense had on more than one occasion decelerated the effort and curtailed the scope—sustaining the sentiment that led Secretary of Defense Wilson to try to eliminate the aircraft nuclear propulsion effort.

The long and short of it was that so far as the United States was officially concerned—nuclear propulsion for space would be better off relegated to a low-priority status, and kept essentially as a "study effort."

By 1960 Brigadier General I. L. Branch, the AEC Assistant Director for Aircraft Reactors, made it clear that a nuclear propulsion booster could be prepared for space flight "in the mid-1960's, without any trouble." But there was another grave problem at the time: just how important was it, in 1960, to get to the moon? Richard E. Horner, Associate Administrator of NASA, ridiculed the idea of a lunar program to send men to the moon within the decade. It would not happen, he explained, until "the time period beyond 1970." And he qualified this forecast with a "perhaps." Since there was no manned lunar expedition effort, and none was forecast for more than ten years, NASA saw little need to emphasize the development of the nuclear space propulsion system. NASA quietly placed the manned lunar expedition on the shelf for future consideration.

AEC's General Branch admitted to the Congress that the nuclear power program was dragging its feet badly. He explained that he was "not completely satisfied" with NASA's requests "for uses of nuclear power." He made it painfully clear that the Rover program was a stepchild of the national space effort. "We can go much faster than they [NASA] want us to go right now."

A major research and study program under way concurrently with Rover was the Department of Defense effort known as Project Orion. This study proposed the use of a huge space platform to be powered with a propulsion system in which a series of one-kiloton (one thousand tons) nuclear blasts would hurl the platform into orbit. Orion also has "enormous possibilities" for deep space missions.

In June of 1960, work on Project Orion was to be terminated within two months because of a shortage of funds. It needed one to two million dollars for one year. At the last moment, the Air Force withdrew $2 million from one of its projects simply to keep Project Orion alive. Congressional officials angrily denounced the Defense Department and NASA's handling of Orion, noting that "NASA has refused to take it over and ARPA, which is in charge of the program, has no plans for continuing it beyond August [1960].

In the following year, Congressman James G. Fulton assailed NASA's procedures in handling Project Rover, when he took off after NASA's contractual activities:

> We have had testimony here that this engine "The Rover" will run either to a half billion or to a billion dollars in cost. That would make the big electrical contractors, with their rigged bids, look like amateurs in a 5- and 10-cent store. If you people, without bidding will receive as a funding basis a guess at what the Rover engine and its components and pumps will cost, give this contract to one of your selected prime contractors, then that prime contractor can coast for years on the Rover project with subcontracts and pass out a half billion to a billion dollars worth of programs with no supervision. I object strongly at this point in the Rover project development to selecting one prime contractor and giving him a billion dollars of the U.S. taxpayers' money without competitive bids as you go along. Let them bid on the components. Let them bid on the pumps. Let them bid on the nozzles. Let them bid on various elements of the engine and not give the whole project over. To me, the Rover project is necessary to the strategic safety of this country. If a single company makes a mistake and the whole thing falls, we are in real trouble. I want competing teams, and I want some of these scientists that are in the teams used, rather than picking a white-haired boy and then working so closely with him that this committee will be unable to find what is going on.
>
> The prime example of that . . . is this McDonnell contract, which started out with $15 to $20 million for the Mercury capsule, then went to $70 to $80 million with installations, and is now up to $210 million.
>
> Of course, some of the committee members have had objections. If this Rover project is starting at a half billion to a billion dollars, and is going to one company, let me know ahead of time. I want to buy the stock.

During late 1960 and in 1961 there was an increased tempo of activity between AEC and NASA. AEC tests with the Kiwi series of reactors and engines proved sufficiently promising for the AEC to increase the rate of propulsion system development with the goal of preparing an actual engine. This would be developed by an industrial contractor who would negotiate concurrently with both NASA and AEC. To pick up any stray program threads, a joint Space Nuclear Propulsion Office (SNPO), staffed with personnel of NASA and AEC, and directed to coordinate the activities of NASA, AEC, and the industrial contractor (or, contractors) in pushing the Rover program, was established in August, 1960.

The creation of this in-house coordinating office tends to mislead the observer as to the pace of progress, which is a far cry from being even satisfactory. From 1956 to 1961, the Los Alamos Laboratory performed "very little significant development . . . on the complex engine components and vehicle designs." Extensive work was indeed carried out, but it remained work that attacked only a part of the over-all problem. Not until mid- or late 1961 did NASA actually commence any serious work on the valves, controls and other engine components for which the space agency is responsible.

At least, however, the goal is now in sight—and it is known as NERVA (Nuclear Engine for Rocket Vehicle Application). Contracts have been awarded to the industrial firms that will produce the NERVA engine and the vehicle to which the engine will be mated for in-flight tests. But while the goal is visible there is yet the heavy hand of slow instead of urgent progress. By mid-1961 NASA was still committed to "a very modest program for follow-on studies for vehicle design and development."

By mid-1961 there was not a single facility in the United States where an experimental nuclear propulsion engine could be tested. Nowhere in the 1961 NASA plans for future development could there be found a single proposal to construct the test facilities where the nuclear vehicle could be fired.

This situation has changed and some planning and construction work was initiated in the NASA-AEC-contractor relationship. However, the situation existed for years after the orbiting of the first Soviet satellites.

When all is said and done, we face the inevitable test of flight scheduling.

Rover was scheduled originally for its first test flight in 1965. Then the schedule slipped, and the new target date of 1966-67 was established. That date has slipped once again—and now Rover is aimed at an initial flight test in the period 1967-68. This final date seems questionable.

Much less open to question and a deep worry in Washington is that the first nuclear rocket to sail the seas of space will be launched from within the USSR.

On October 1, 1962, NASA Administrator James E. Webb, in fine oratory fettle, complained that: "I sometimes find it difficult to understand, in a nation which has repeatedly demonstrated its capacity to achieve supremacy in any technological effort, when it is determined to do so, why expressions of confidence in our ability to lead in space should be greeted with doubt, disbelief, or suspicion."

When the President speaks on matters of great national interest and import we listen to his words with great attention. President Kennedy has brought to the Executive position an astounding candor on where we stand with the Russians in rocket booster power. He has laid it right on the line—they're ahead, and they will be for some time to come, but we're determined to catch the opposition and then to surpass them.

Fair enough. But what is difficult to swallow is the statement that: "We choose to go to the moon in this decade, and do the other things, not because they are easy, but because they are hard, because that goal will serve to organize and measure the best of our energy and skills."

That is an interesting statement; it is also pure and unadulterated politics, with barely a shred of reality attached to it. We choose to go to the moon in this decade, because there isn't any doubt in anyone's mind that the Russians are going toward the moon with hard, driving energy and we're more than a little concerned about that still lengthening distance between ourselves and the Russians in space. That's the main reason for our being in the race. Not that there aren't many other reasons—it is just that none of them, scientific or otherwise, have ever lent any impetus to our decision to strike out for the moon in this decade.

Few people were more surprised at our national decision to reach the moon by 1970 than NASA officials. After all, they were the ones who were responsible for the program—and they swore under oath to the Congress that they didn't even contemplate such a thing until well into the 1970's.

The Apollo program which we hope will convey three astronauts to the dusty surface of the moon will undoubtedly cost the United States somewhere on the order of thirty billion dollars or more. In 1962 the United States began frenzied preparations for the great adventure to the moon. Only a year before, it had laughed at the idea, and didn't go to any trouble to get hardware development under way. Why should NASA do this? Obviously, the moon would not be accessible to us in this decade—it might just as well be a million or a billion miles away. We weren't even going to *try*.

When Dr. Hugh Dryden testified before the Congress on appropriations for Apollo in the spring of 1961 he made it very clear that: "There are no hardware funds in this. They are for the solution of the problems that are involved."

Let us examine the hardware program that *was* under way in 1960—the case of the great Saturn I * booster, the rocket with a first-stage thrust of 1,500,000 pounds. In its I version with a

---

* NASA in early 1963 redesignated all of its major boosters: Saturn C-1 became Saturn I, Saturn C-1B became Saturn IB, and Saturn C-5 became Saturn V.

second stage, Saturn will boost 20,000 pounds into earth orbit. In the IB version, with a more powerful second stage, Saturn will send 28,000 pounds into earth orbit.

The Saturn I vehicle series is indispensable to our lunar program. If a current planning schedule hews to its hopes, then by late 1964 or early 1965 the Saturn I will be boosting Apollo spaceship command modules, and astronauts, into earth orbit. It will also fill the holes created by the crippling failure of Centaur and will give us the means to match the payload of Mars I that the Russians launched in 1962.

But Saturn wasn't always known by this name; originally it was the Army's Juno V, a booster rocket of clustered engines that began in the summer of 1958. At that time a group of Army engineers considered the concept of clustering seven to nine rocket engines in order to build a single booster of at least 1,500,000 pounds thrust. The engines from the Jupiter ballistic missile held the greatest promise. They were proven, available, reliable, required a minimum of modification, promised low costs, and could be mated in a single package in the shortest possible time.

Roy Johnson, as the head of ARPA, in August 1958 gave his informal authorization for the study program to proceed. The Army went to the ballistic missile center at Huntsville, Alabama, and discussed the idea with Dr. Wernher von Braun. The German scientist responded with his own design of four 380,000-pound thrust engines, but admitted that employing the more powerful rockets would multiply costs and development time. Official histories credit von Braun as receiving the proposal for eight clustered engines with open arms, especially because of a unique reliability factor. With eight engines firing, the booster would be so designed that the loss of any one engine would not compromise the mission. The propellants would be shunted to the other engines. Although there would be less total thrust available, the burning time of the rocket in flight would be extended and final performance achieved.

Despite what may have been said of von Braun's enthusiasm,

this does not fit neatly into the true picture. Dr. von Braun accepted the clustered rockets, but apparently more for the availability of the final vehicle than for its inherent engineering superiority. In the spring of 1958, discussing the clustered-engine booster with a Congressional committee, von Braun explained that it would be preferable to use one big engine rather than several engines. He admitted readily: "It is possible, of course, to get a million pounds thrust out of clusters of the most powerful engines we have today. . . . you would need about seven of them to get a million pounds, approximately. It can be done this way, but *it is not a very good way of doing it* [emphasis added] because the cluster of seven engines contains so many components that you lose reliability. . . . Also, clustering is very heavy."

It would seem appropriate to keep von Braun's remarks in mind when reading NASA press releases describing Saturn I as the most advanced booster design today. Also, it is pertinent to note that von Braun describes clustering as "very heavy." A rocket that achieves 1,500,000 pounds thrust through a single engine, for example, will deliver performance superior to that of a rocket producing the same thrust through eight engines with the heavy, complicated engine mechanisms and mounts. This is a point to consider when comparing, for example, the performance of a Russian booster with Saturn I, which has the same thrust. The Russian booster uses fewer engines and is lighter in weight. It will outperform Saturn I.

In 1958, however, the clustered booster held the greatest promise for an immediate return in great rocket power if the program were pressed with greatest possible speed. At first it appeared that we would have this sense of urgency and we did. It did not require many more months, however, before the familiar tearing of the program fabric began to show.

By the end of August 1958, ARPA had funded $15 million for the booster. Three months later bickering began to stall the program. In November NASA and ARPA officials held preliminary reviews of the forthcoming budgets of the two agencies.

A result of this joint NASA-ARPA meeting was a recommendation that the program for the 1,500,000-pound-thrust booster *be canceled*. The two factions did not see eye to eye on the needs and purposes of Saturn, and one way to solve all arguments was simply to forget the whole thing despite the fact that this would leave the United States without a booster any more powerful than the Atlas, or the forthcoming Titan II missile (scheduled for operational use in mid-1963). The cancellation was rejected and the groups discussed the matter of transferring Saturn from ARPA jurisdiction into the NASA fold. Roy Johnson angrily opposed this move and left no doubts but that he would fight to retain the booster. Dr. T. Keith Glennan, then the NASA Administrator, deferred any conflict by washing his hands of the matter. NASA had no plans for a large booster, didn't need the booster, and he was little concerned over its disposition.

Roy Johnson may one day become a legend in Washington. In the face of strong opposition to Saturn, he not only succeeded in retaining the booster under his jurisdiction but also managed to increase the funds appropriated for the vehicle as a military booster of extreme importance to defense requirements.

On December 9, 1958, the Army Ballistic Missile Agency requested that a DX priority be assigned to the Saturn I booster. The Department of Defense lacked the convictions of Roy Johnson or the Army, and refused assignment of the industrial priority.

As work progressed, and Army engineers began their program of developing suitable upper stages for Saturn, von Braun and his staff set the month of October 1960 as their target for the first Saturn flight test.* They planned for two tests of the main booster, and for shots three and four they scheduled live upper stages and planned to send heavy payloads into orbit about the earth (this

* Although optimistic in their expectations—program delays encountered were not of their making—the von Braun group achieved a perfect success in the first Saturn flight test on October 27, 1961, only one year behind the original schedule.

is now scheduled for 1964). The fifth Saturn flight would carry a Centaur third stage for sending a heavy probe to the moon; the reader already acquainted with the Centaur program will understand why no further comment is necessary on that matter.

In May 1959, with program development moving steadily ahead, the Army again requested assignment of the DX priority. And, as before, the Department of Defense turned down the request.

By July 1959, Saturn was in deep trouble. Dr. Herbert York of the Department of Defense apparently had been rubbed the wrong way long enough by the Saturn program. He stated flatly that Saturn was a program for which the United States had no present need, and would not have a need in the foreseeable future. Dr. York claimed that the Air Force's Titan C booster rocket (a paper proposal that subsequently was committed to the waste basket) would attend to all national booster requirements. Dr. York submitted his decision in writing to Roy Johnson at ARPA: "I have decided to cancel the Saturn program on the grounds that there is no military justification therefor. . . ."

Once again the persuasive arguments of Roy Johnson prevailed, and Saturn gained another precarious lease on life. But only for a brief period. In the fall of 1959 the question of military support of Saturn again arose. The Department of Defense made it painfully clear that it had decided that the military budget simply could not afford to sustain the Saturn program. There did not exist a single specified mission (Centaur was scheduled for the Advent military communications satellite) for Saturn, and none could be predicted with so great a need as to justify continuing the program.

NASA received, along with control of the Army Ballistic Missile Agency, the Saturn booster program. Saturn came along into the NASA fold not as a requirement of high priority—but simply as so much excess baggage. The transfer to NASA of the Saturn program, warned Roy Johnson, was a move without any really inherent justification. It would solve nothing in respect to national booster rocket needs, and Johnson cautioned that in the long run it would actually impose another severe financial burden on the economy. Early in 1960 he explained his thinking to the Congress:

> The concern I have had about transferring Saturn to NASA was that by so doing, since the Air Force has now been given primary military responsibility for space programs, that the Air Force would then begin to create its own system, including its own booster, and it is possible, unless you gentlemen watch this very closely, that we will be going down the road of developing another multibillion [dollar] space system to put Dyna-Soar into orbit—to do many other things—and the military will not use the Saturn project, and we will have two parallel programs. . . . I think that the giving of this Saturn to NASA has made the possibility of even greater expense to the country and the development of a new weapons system more probable.

In the late summer of 1962, with the orbiting of the two cosmonauts Nikolayev and Popovich still a painful memory in Washington, Defense Secretary Robert McNamara authorized the Air Force to move ahead with a crash priority program to develop the Titan III—a huge Titan II missile with enormous solid-propellant rockets lashed to its sides. With several million pounds' thrust, Titan III could send a 32,000-pound payload into orbit and would be used for the Dyna-Soar aerospace plane development program.

Saturn in the meantime had enjoyed all the benefits of great engineering competence from the von Braun group in Alabama, but it had not escaped the knife of budgetary cutbacks. From 1958 until the spring of 1960, budget cuts totaled $163 million. At that time von Braun stated that the loss of these funds had already caused the irretrievable loss of more than six months in bringing Saturn to operational status.

Once within the NASA fold, Saturn was looked upon as the end of the road in booster development for perhaps the next decade. It must be remembered that NASA specifically did not plan a manned expedition to the moon for at least another ten to fifteen years, and despite great booster potential among industry, the Saturn I in the official NASA opinion was the top of the booster mountain. NASA Administrator Dr. T. Keith Glennan made this point clear in 1960 when he stated:

> There gets to be a limit to this sort of thing. We have the Saturn laid on as a base rocket of a million-and-a-half pounds thrust. We have upper stages . . . that will be in the liquid oxygen-liquid hydrogen class, which give us a very high specific impulse. This should result in the development of a really powerful system. It ought to put up as much weight as anybody really would want to put up. And I doubt that the Soviets will exceed that.*

In 1960, the NASA Administrator outlined the plans of the national space agency for the coming decade. During the next ten years, explained Dr. Glennan, NASA would spend some $12 billion, and for this amount we would buy "leadership in the space field." This amount of money would also assure that we would "regain the confidence of the entire world in the quality of leadership [and] scientific competence."

That was 1960. At the rate of spending of fiscal 1963, NASA will expend the costs for an entire decade of space research in less than two years. The estimate of $12 billion for the entire decade won't even pay for half the cost of placing two men on the moon and that's assuming that we will stop everything else going on in the national space program. Obviously, planning for the space future lacked a sense of realism.

The American gamble to reach the moon in this decade—in a wild and unrestrained moment of joyous optimism, some NASA

* In 1962 the Russians operationally fired boosters at least equal to, and perhaps exceeding, the deep-space mission capability of Saturn I.
In 1962 the United States—NASA, specifically—was engaged in a maximum priority, multi-billion-dollar effort to build the Saturn V, with a capability of placing into earth orbit a payload of *240,000 pounds,* or sending a spaceship weighing 90,000 pounds to the moon.

officials said by 1966 or 1967—depends upon a rocket engine known as F-1. This is a single combustion chamber that produces as much thrust as the entire first stage of Saturn I. The Apollo spaceship will be boosted to the moon by a Saturn V vehicle. In the first stage there will be five F-1 motors, to generate 7,500,000 pounds' thrust. Five J-2 liquid hydrogen motors in the second stage will add another 1,000,000 pounds' thrust, and a third stage of a single J-2 will wrap up the package with a final push of 200,000 pounds' thrust. Assembled on the launch pad, the monster will stand about 380 feet high, and will rest ponderously on its launch stand with a weight of more than six million pounds.

We are engaged at the moment in a frenzied push to bring the F-1 engine to operational status. There isn't a schoolboy in America who hasn't heard of the F-1, who doesn't know that this is the key to walking across the lunar surface. What the schoolboys and their fathers don't know is that until recently the F-1 engine couldn't even find a place to hide within the NASA organization. NASA officials wished it would go away quietly. They had no use for the engine, except for some dim and unspecified time in the following decade.

The F-1 first existed as an Air Force engine development program, part of the package shipped over to NASA soon after it assumed the role of space leadership for the country. NASA did its best to keep the F-1 out of its official hair. Yet, NASA vacillated between explanations of the F-1 engine as useful only for a long-range study program and requesting the highest national priority in the country to push its development.

The Congress in July of 1960 made special note of this inconsistency: *

> The F-1 project, to develop a single chamber rocket engine of 1.5 million pounds thrust, fundamental to the Nova concept, has never been given a top priority. According to Dr.

---

* "Space, Missiles, and the Nation," Report No. 2092 of the Committee on Science and Astronautics, House of Representatives, July 5, 1960.

T. Keith Glennan, Administrator of NASA, a DX priority is not needed. Dr. Glennan so testified before the committee on January 29. . . .

Yet prior to this Dr. Glennan and his advisers felt so strongly about getting a DX priority for the big engine project that after taking the matter up with the Defense Department on November 14, 1958, they carried their request for a top priority to the National Aeronautics and Space Council, which turned it down on December 3, 1958.

Subsequently, on March 17, 1960, the NASA disclosed that the F-1 engine program was delayed because of difficulty in obtaining steel during the steel strike. A DX priority would perhaps have prevented this, since some steel was available during the strike for top priority programs.

The attention focused on the critical importance of the F-1 engine today is in stark contrast to the offhand manner in which this project was treated within NASA. Dr. Glennan in discussing possible uses of the F-1 (in March 1960) made this point clear when he explained:

There has not been designed a rocket system which will use the F-1 engine. . . . Until we get more realistic information on the development results of the F-1 engine, it is really not too useful to go on beyond conceptual studies of the design of the vehicle configuration. We will have time, when we know that the engine is really going down the line well—and it seems to be thus far—we will have time to design this. As a matter of fact, I think studies are starting this year . . .

But while NASA talked of "conceptual designs" and the need to gain "more realistic information" on F-1 development, it had pursued a course that pushed the F-1 further from final development. NASA Associate Administrator Richard E. Horner claimed that the F-1 program had suffered a crippling blow because of Congressional slashes in the funds authorized in 1959 for this program. The delays would mean a loss in development time of perhaps eighteen months, Mr. Horner said. This meant that instead of a development time of forty-two months for the F-1, this could well mean a stretch in the program to five and a half years.

But Mr. Horner also indicated that the F-1 engine remained far down on NASA's own list of priorities. Because of a loss of some $18 million in NASA research and development funds, the space agency itself cut the F-1 program by $6 million. The Congress noted that "Mr. Horner admitted that NASA traded a year or a year and a half on the development of the F-1 engine for $6 million."

When the United States made its decision to strike out for the moon, with the hope of landing two men on the surface of that alien body, and returning them safely to earth, it did so on the basis that we had a great deal to learn about the extremely powerful engine systems that would be needed. The President called for a parallel course of research and development in both liquid and solid propulsion systems.

Up until this time the program to develop the high-energy solid-propellant motor had been the most unsubstantial element of our national space effort. This was not because of a lack of knowledge or capability. Industrial and scientific proponents of solid-propellant motors had been clawing at the walls in Washington offices, trying to get this kind of effort on its feet. Their efforts proved of little avail. Yet there could not be denied the insistent and rising clamor from many sources about the lack of a solid-propellant booster program. Top-flight engineers, rankled by the months going by without any true action, put their careers on the line. By 1964, they said, we could have boosters that would carry manned spaceships to the moon.

They did not deny basic advantages in liquid-propellant engine systems. However, they emphasized that combinations of the solid and liquid systems, with the solids providing the power to lift the first stage from earth, could enable us to leapfrog Soviet booster power within only a few years.

On March 23, 1961, during Congressional hearings for the authorization of 1962 NASA appropriations, Congressman David S. King tried to cut through the murkiness of confusion and evasion on the matter of the solid-propellant booster effort. The Congressman made little effort to conceal his growing impatience with the casual attitude of NASA on the subject:

> ... We have had testimony in this committee by the advocates and devotees of solid-fuel propellant that, given proper funding and proper authorization, they could deliver a 21,000,000-pound thrust vehicle within 2 to 3 years. This disturbs me because this fact seems so palpably at variance with the existing schedule that has already been worked out and which you [NASA officials] have so clearly given us this morning. I have asked the question before: Are the proper Government officials trying to resolve this controversy; is the machinery in motion by the proper NASA officials to set at rest, once and for all, the question as to whether the solid-fuel devotees can get a solid-fuel missile in the air within 2 or 3 years? The answer that has come back to me is invariably "Yes; we have the machinery set into motion to resolve this controversy." I must confess I have not seen any evidence that the machinery is in motion to resolve the controversy. And everything that has been presented ... suggests that NASA is proceeding on the theory that the claims of the solid-fuel propellant people are not worthy of being considered, at least so far as the 1962 budget is concerned. I must say I am a little shocked that NASA has seemed to have taken so casually what would seem to be very significant and historic claims by the solid-fuel propellant people.

More than one year later the Congress found so little reason to change its attitude that it instigated a full-dress investigation into what seemed to be both mismanagement and a deliberate slowdown of the program.

The national effort in solid boosters called for a joint NASA-DOD effort amounting to $158.3 million, which was to be supervised and managed by the Air Force. Congress readily provided the funds but DOD officials shortly thereafter decided to downgrade the program substantially, and withheld assignment of much of this money to the Air Force. Congressmen changed their attitudes from disenchantment to anger, for they had authorized the appropriations, only to learn that DOD had overruled them, and that NASA was failing to sustain the wishes of the Congress, with the end result that the solid booster program once again was lagging.

Two major types of booster motors were under development, known as the 156-inch and the 240- or 260-inch models. What finally blew the lid off the mismanagement of the program was the fact that the Department of Defense had stopped the development of both. Repeated questions by Committee members to ascertain specifically whether or not the development of these motors was under way were met without success. Over and over again the question was asked: ". . . what is the present status of the 156-inch and the 240-inch program? What is the status of these two motor development programs?"

The answers left the Committee more than a little confused, for the replies were couched in such terms as "We are now in the process of reviewing the approach to these programs in terms of the experimental endeavor that is to be carried out."

Since the Congressmen were responsible for providing the funds requested by NASA for work in this, and other, areas, they were understandably irritated by the inability to get specific answers to specific questions. Congressman James G. Fulton stated flatly that he was both "disappointed" and "discouraged" at NASA's conduct in the matter. He reiterated to NASA officials that he could not find any "set schedule for programming, for reaching various plateaus of accomplishment, that would lead us on to a development program." Knifing deeper into the morass of confusion, Congressman Fulton assailed NASA's indecisions that had led to dangerous stretchouts in the solid booster program. He added:

... you hope to get a program but you haven't got it now, and it must then be agreed on by the DOD and by NASA, but to date there is no agreement. It is simply a hope that some program will be mutually acceptable to both, and then you hope "to the best interests of the space program." Now that doesn't say whether it is the NASA program, the military program, or the overall U.S. space program.

You say further: "We are presently working with the DOD in an effort to establish in detail a mutually acceptable program for review by higher authority."

Which again emphasized that there is no approved program now, because you are going to try to establish it for review by higher authority.

... your statements do not give us the timing, the levels of accomplishment of the program, nor the development of these various motors, configurations, fuels, or program funding.

NASA officials came back with the old saw that: "Funds are always short for these sorts of programs..." And that simply raised the boiling point in the Committee room, with an angry retort from Congressman Fulton that—"They are not always short, because I am not the only one on this Committee that had put in an amendment to give NASA more money for solid fuel research. As a matter of fact, when NASA came in once with a justification for $8.3 million, by amendment we increased it to $18.3 million, $10 million more than was asked."

The Committee members reminded NASA that if they *were* short on money, "you certainly are a little late in telling us." Which seems to be an eminently fair response, since the 1963 NASA program was passed in the House by a vote of 342 to 0.

Congressman David S. King peeled away another layer of acute dissatisfaction. He expressed serious concern about the transfer of responsibility of solid-fuel boosters from NASA to the Air Force. He insisted that there was something "basically wrong" in the activities that had occurred to date. He reminded the NASA officials that the military had a specific mission, and NASA had its specific mission. Warming to the subject, he emphasized the following:

> Getting to the Moon is not a military mission. . . . our official position as of now and in the foreseeable future is that anything we do in outer space is strictly nonmilitary. Outer space is for peaceful purposes.
>
> The National Aeronautics and Space Administration is the agency that is charged with carrying out this nonmilitary, this peaceful mission into space. Getting to the Moon is the very heart and core of that mission. That is our big target. . . .
>
> So if we turn this over to the Air Force whose responsibility is our defense, not beating the Russians to the Moon, I wonder myself whether they are going to have the proper motivation. This is your responsibility, it seems to me, and not theirs.
>
> I can understand you using their technology. They are experts in this field. They have developed the Minuteman and the Navy has developed Polaris, and they have some knowhow in this field. I can well understand your using it. The thing that puzzles me is why you should turn over the main responsibility for vigorously pursuing this program when it seems to me that Congress and the law has made it very clear that that responsibility rests at the doorstep of the National Aeronautics and Space Administration.

.   .   .   .

> Last year I had the distinct impression from what President Kennedy said in his state of the Union message as it was supplemented by other messages, I had the distinct impression that we were to pursue a parallel course of R. & D. in both liquids and solids. I wouldn't say $14 million compared to the hundreds of millions that have gone into liquid is exactly a parallel course of development. I wonder if what has actually happened in practice has been carried out in good faith.

Its hearings completed with NASA, the Congress turned to the Air Force, and tried, as it had tried with futile results before, to obtain specific answers as to the program status with the 156- and 260-inch solid motors. The Committee put the question to General Bernard A. Schriever, who replied: "There are no contracts out now that can be said to be specifically directed toward the 156- and the 260-inch application. There is, of course, a lot of work going on in the solid-propellant area that has a bearing on them, but the answer to your question is: 'No, there is not.' "

At this writing the solid-motor program has at long last—but on shaky feet—received its first development contracts, as part of the Air Force Titan III booster development effort.

CHAPTER **16.**

THE IMPORTANCE OF
DECISION-MAKING

IT is obvious that our preparations for, and our response to, the age of space leave much to be desired. In 1962 the United States made its "great decisions" in terms of exploring the moon. *Project Apollo* shifted from paper studies to contractual and hardware development status. The joy at this abrupt acceleration of our effort was boundless, and there was felt throughout all the organizations and the people involved a ringing sense of urgency, and a conviction that we were in the process of creating a juggernaut for the conquest of space.

As the new year began, however, it became obvious to the observer of these preparations that we were witnessing the first signs of the unraveling of the fabric. The shouting was over, the hard work had begun, and the expenditure of vast sums of money became an accounting matter. And soon afterward, like a runner who is good for the sprint but weak for the long pull, our program quickly began to slow down. The year 1962 was not over when NASA began to slip from the schedule which it had so firmly established for the manned lunar landing. And already we were witnessing several months forever gone in this "most urgent" of national goals.

Orders went out to industrial contractors to slow down. Despite the billions of dollars budgeted for the NASA program, an economy drive drilled quickly through it. By the end of 1962, the evidence was clear that we lost seven months from the "crash program" for the moon landing. And we will lose much more.

Project Mercury is vital to gathering biomedical data and engineering experience in order that we might progress rapidly from this dead-end program to the Apollo lunar program. When astronaut John Glenn returned in triumph from his mission in space, NASA spoke confidently of astronaut flights every ninety days. Wally Schirra orbited the earth in October of 1962. Gordon Cooper is not scheduled to rocket above this world until May or June of 1963, at the earliest. The time from Schirra to Cooper is substantially longer than ninety days.

In order to conserve its funds, NASA has not only delayed and decelerated the scope of many of its activities, but it has also delayed the confirmation and assignment of several major projects. Economy is dictating the pace for the two-man Gemini capsule. At the close of 1962, it had become obvious that the scheduled flight program for Gemini would slip by four months at the least. NASA ordered a slowdown in preparation for the powerful Titan II booster, which will send the 7,000-pound Gemini into orbit. The manufacturer of the Titan II booster, responding to the economy measures, laid off several hundred workers. In the early months of 1963, Gemini slipped again. The first manned flights were scheduled for some time in 1964. And budget shortages were creating "merry hell" with even this stretched-out schedule.

At Cape Canaveral the pace of construction for the critical launch facilities for the Saturn boosters in the Apollo program has been cut back. Contractors have been told to stretch out their scheduling. Minimum loss of time: four to eight months. It is also apparent that a shortage of funds necessitating an across-the-board economy drive of this nature in our most critical of space projects, will affect sharply the progress in other areas.

It is distressing to see how quickly the momentum created in the summer and fall of 1962 may be lost. The final result may be a loss of much more than time.

Dr. Harrison Brown, the brilliant American scientist, member of the Space Science Board of the National Academy of Sciences, summed it up on his return from the Soviet Union. Dr. Brown had recently completed a remarkable stay in the USSR, where he was a guest of the Soviet Academy of Sciences so he might study the methods by which the USSR makes its final decisions in the matters of scientific and technological programs.

I was permitted to study the detailed structure of the Academy there, how decisions are made vis-a-vis the Academy and the new coordinating committee with respect to science and technology and its interrelationships to the Soviet Council of Ministers and the structures of several of the academies within the various Soviet Republics. And I must say, although their system is certainly quite different from ours, one must say with respect to certain kinds of problems, it is enormously effective and in certain areas almost breathtaking. Particularly when it comes to the speed with which they are able to operate once they make the decision to put their efforts behind a certain kind of project.

I was the first American, I believe, to be permitted to go out to central Siberia and visit this new science city which they are constructing and which is now [1961] partially in operation.

It reminded me somewhat of Oak Ridge in the early days of the war. It has been put up with a speed comparable to the speed with which Oak Ridge was established. It is, however, a more permanent type of housing. They are constructing fifteen major research institutes and a major university, and when it is completed in another two years, they will have a population of about thirty thousand.

The university is designed to feed technical people into the institutes.

Now, I just cite this as an example of the scale and the kinds of operations that are going on there. They are able to take these steps by virtue of their own kind of decision-making capability. Our whole approach to this problem is quite a different one, and I believe that now the task that confronts us is how we can make the proper decisions in the legislative branch of Government . . .

Which is perhaps another way of saying that the speed and accuracy of making decisions is much more important than the speed and accuracy of all the rockets we will ever fire into space.

EPILOGUE

THE moon in the year 1969 is not a lifeless world. For billions of years nothing stirred on this barren graveyard of a planet; but now there is life. It is not indigenous to the moon, it comes from another world. That world hangs in the sky as a brilliant blue-white sphere, its surface splayed with the scudding streaks of its cloud formations. It is from the surface of Earth that men departed to cross the seas of space. And now they walk the moon.

Near the lunar equator there is an unlovely assembly of buildings. They are metallic, crude, but efficient in their purpose. Gleaming steel doors in the side of a steep cliff reveal the airlocks that lead to more permanent quarters within the bowels of the rock.

The moon is hostile. It is uncompromising toward errors in attempts to survive. It is a hard vacuum, an amphitheater naked to cosmic rays and the silent impact of meteoric dust and particles. But the men who have been here on the moon for more than two years are accustomed to the hardships, the nakedness of their environment. They have learned to live with its dangers. And they are digging in. The process is slow and tortuous, but from the earth they have brought a small nuclear reactor for power, and have learned to tap raw solar energy for more power, and deep within their caverns they sustain and nourish the first agricultural beds on the moon. They crush rock for raw materials and for water. The process is expensive, and they are still dependent for much of their needs upon the earth.

But it is obvious that they have come here to stay.

Strange tracked vehicles with bulbous control cabs are parked about the base camp. Some distance away powerful spaceships, hulking on their long legs, stand in a cleared area. The initials on the sides of the spaceships read C.C.C.P. (USSR).

There is excitement in the camp today. Confirmation has been received of another rocket on its way to the moon, a rocket carrying men. On the side of that rocket are painted the words *United States.*

Two days later that rocket is seen falling toward the moon. It turns and adjusts its attitude as it falls. Brilliant tongues of flame wink into existence, controlling and modifying the descent. Finally, the rocket stabs downward with a long tongue of flame. Exhaust gases knife into the lunar surface. Dust and gravel shower outward, without a sound, in a great cloud. Still without a sound, the cloud begins to fall back toward the moon. The spaceship touches down. The flame dies out.

The two Americans slowly climb down the side of their spaceship. Far off in the distance they can see lights moving. Two surface crawlers; Russian vehicles on the way to the landing site. The Americans report by radio back to earth of the imminent, historic greeting.

It is historic, it is not unexpected, but it is overwhelming in its implications. The Russians and the Americans tune their spacesuit radio sets to the same frequencies. The Soviet commander speaks flawless English.

He does not greet the Americans.

In a cold voice he makes an announcement. He speaks for the Government of the USSR. By all the precedents and the traditions of exploration, the moon is a territory belonging to the USSR. The Russian commander makes this point very clear. The flag has been planted. A permanent colony has been here for two years.

This is a possession of the Soviet Union. The Americans are not welcome. The sight of several Russians holding high-velocity rifles, a devastating weapon under lunar surface conditions, makes this point very clear.

The Russian commander does not mince words. He orders the Americans to leave at once. He will allow them the time to make whatever computations are necessary so that their departure can be made in safety. But no longer, or their spacecraft will be confiscated, and they will be taken prisoners. Resistance would be, very obviously, futile.

Several hours later, there is again the sight of flame on the surface of the moon. This time the flame ascends, shrinks in size as the American spaceship heads back for earth.

The Russians return to their camp. An aide remarks to the base commander that he is surprised. He was certain that the Americans would not respond to the orders to get off the moon. He admits that there was nothing that they could do at the moment, but certainly there will be trouble later.

The base commander looks at him and shakes his head.

"No," he says, "there will be no trouble. We have a great lead over the Americans. We are here with a complete base. They are just starting."

He looks up at the great swollen ball of Earth hanging in the black sky. "But that is not the issue," he continues. "There will be no trouble because of another reason.

"Do you think that the Americans would risk a war with hydrogen bombs over the moon?

"I assure you—this they will not do. This battle—which will never be fought—was won by us years ago."

APPENDIX

SPACE RESEARCH MISSIONS

FROM December 6, 1957, when the first Vanguard rocket rose several inches, then fell back with a flaming blast to its launching pad, until December 1, 1962, the United States attempted to fire into space more than 160 satellites, lunar probes, and deep space probes. Obviously, not all of these were successful. The launching record in the early years of the space program left much to be desired.

In 1958, for example, we attempted seventeen space missions. Only five of these met their goal. The other twelve, even though we claimed several as "partial successes," went on the failure list.

In 1959, our record improved. Of nineteen shots, ten succeeded and nine failed. We were finally batting just over .500.

The year 1960 showed yet another gain in reliability and success. Thirteen shots failed, but sixteen succeeded.

This did not represent the full picture. As we acquired larger booster vehicles, we attempted more complicated and demanding experiments. As the requirements for each shot soared, the possibilities of failure also increased. For example, a lunar probe experiment that failed as a probe worked perfectly as an earth satellite. If this had been our goal, we could mark the score sheet as completely successful. As to deep-space and lunar probes, we failed.

Similarly, the score sheet in numbers alone also misleads us. The number of satellites placed in orbit means little, unless we can utilize them. Obviously, ten satellites each weighing 100 pounds do not give us the same capability as a single satellite weighing 1,000 pounds. It may be that the experiment is to test a new stabilization system that weighs 600 pounds. If the biggest satellite you can put up weighs only 100 pounds, the experiment is impossible. And all the publicity in the world about the total number of satellites cannot escape this fact.

However, what we are seeking in space is a matter that escapes many people. For the record, then, here is a cross-representation of satellite shots—and the missions intended for the payloads of those satellites. Not all our satellite missions are included, since many simply repeat previous shots to acquire greater data in a particular field. Also several dozen of Air Force Samos and Midas satellites have gone successfully into orbit. Many of them carry scientific instruments in addition to their military equipment, and many of them also have been recovered from orbit, but the results of these missions have been declared classified. We can, however, include the test results of Air Force Discoverer satellites, which combine equipment technology, military developments, spacecraft capabilities, and scientific research.

EXPLORER I: January 31, 1958

Our first satellite went into orbit with 18 pounds of instruments, sweeping as high as 1,155 miles above the earth. The original objectives were to place a satellite in Earth orbit for studies of micrometeorites, cosmic rays, and temperature measurements. Explorer I turned in some unexpected results, notably the discovery of the Van Allen Radiation Belt, believed to be the most significant new finding of the IGY. In addition, the satellite demonstrated the feasibility of controlling metal temperatures in space by treating the metal in different forms. Scientists concluded from data transmitted to Earth that "micrometeorites are not a major consideration in space travel near Earth."

EXPLORER III: March 26, 1958

Carrying 18.56 pounds of instruments, Explorer III orbited the earth from a perigee of 117 miles to an apogee of 1,741 miles. The elliptical orbit was sought to continue the study of micrometeorite conditions in space, as well as to record intensities of cosmic rays. Additional instruments measured temperatures within and on the outer surface of the satellite. The results were "valuable data on radiation belts and micrometeor impacts as well as external and internal temperatures."

EXPLORER IV: July 26, 1958

With information accumulating from previous satellites on the characteristics of the radiation belts in space, scientists used Explorer IV to seek out more refined data. This was also our first satellite to measure the effects of man-made forces on the space environment. Small atomic bombs from Project Argus had been exploded in space, and Explorer IV telemetered back valuable information on the formation and characteristics of these belts. The scientists listed this satellite as extremely helpful in establishing "detailed spatial relationships" and for providing information on the "properties of Argus radiation." This in turn "aided in analyses of Earth's magnetic field."

PROJECT SCORE: December 18, 1958

A powerful Atlas missile provided the means to conduct a multi-mission space test. In the first orbiting of an entire Atlas ICBM, engineers established the feasibility of the missile as a space booster. At the same time they placed a 150-pound communications package aboard the Atlas. For the first time a human voice, via tape recorder, was beamed from space to the earth. The results of this mission were manifold: feasibility of the Atlas; atmospheric density studies by noting the orbital decay period of the Atlas; and communications acceptance and relay between the Atlas and ground stations.

VANGUARD II and III: February 17 and September 18, 1959

These two satellites demonstrate the difficulty of obtaining information from charts or lists of satellite missions. Vanguard II went into a high elliptical orbit extending to several thousand miles from the earth at its apogee. NASA orbited the 21.5-pound payload for studies of the cloud cover of the planet. Although the satellite went into its desired orbit, it wobbled as it moved instead of achieving a stable attitude. This wobble "prevented interpretation of cloud cover data." In other words, the orbiting mission proved successful—the scientific mission failed.

Vanguard III, placed in an elliptical orbit (perigee of 320 miles and apogee of 2,320 miles) on September 18, 1959, proved an unexpected bonanza. The original maximum payload of Vanguard was 21.5 pounds, but this satellite carried 50 pounds of instruments. Vanguard III's mission called for a general survey of magnetic fields, solar X-rays, micrometeorites, and temperature levels in space. All missions were met, and scientific studies concluded that Vanguard III "provided a comprehensive survey of Earth's magnetic field over areas covered; detailed location of lower edge of Van Allen Radiation Belt; accurate count of micrometeorite impacts."

DISCOVERER II: April 13, 1959

This second in the highly successful Air Force satellite series demonstrated a long-term development mission. The Discoverer vehicles could produce information unobtainable from satellites launched from Cape Canaveral. Discoverers lifted from Vandenberg Air Force Base in California, and then went into polar orbits—north to south. As they orbited in this direction, the earth rotated beneath them and provided complete coverage of the entire surface of the planet, and the space environment above the globe.

The Discoverer series developed a system of satellite capabilities for other vehicles and programs. Initially their orbital missions were to "gather data on propulsion, communications, orbital performance, stabilization, recovery techniques, and measurement of cosmic radiation." Discoverer II achieved a near-circular polar orbit. Equally, if not more important, automatic sensors and controls aboard the satellite stabilized the vehicle in reference to the horizon of the earth.

EXPLORER VI: August 7, 1959

Into this 142-pound satellite, a spheroid with four large "paddlewheel" solar-cell vanes for electrical power from the sun, went instruments to measure three specific radiation levels of Earth Radiation Belts; to test a scanning device for studying the Earth's cloud cover; to measure micrometeorites; and, to study the behavior of radio waves. The orbit was a huge ellipse; the satellite circled the globe from a perigee of

156 miles to an apogee of 26,357 miles, and provided a clear demonstration of changing velocities in space. As it swooped close to the earth, Explorer VI accelerated to 23,031 miles per hour; but at its peak altitude it slowed to only 3,126 miles per hour. Scientists were overjoyed with the tests, for the satellite carried out all experiments and relayed the data clearly to ground stations. The official report noted that we had achieved the "first complete televised cloud-picture" of the Earth, that the instruments "detected a large ring of electrical current circling the Earth; and that scientists for the first time obtained a "complete map of the Van Allen Radiation Belt."

EXPLORER VII: October 13, 1959

With a payload of 91.5 pounds, this satellite was given the mission of conducting several radiation studies and obtaining counts of micrometeor impacts against its surface. It carried sensors for measurement of the heat balance of the Earth-Sun system; Lyman-Alpha and X-ray solar radiation detectors; micrometeor detectors; Geiger-Muller tubes for cosmic ray count; and an ionization chamber for detecting heavy cosmic rays. Once again the results proved outstanding. Explorer VII provided a wealth of "significant geophysical information on radiation and magnetic storms; demonstrated a method of controlling internal temperatures; recorded the first micrometeorite penetration of a sensor in flight; and showed detection of large-scale weather patterns."

TIROS I: April 1, 1960

The first of the United States' meteorological satellites, Tiros I weighed 270 pounds, and appeared as a pillbox covered on its tops and sides with 9,200 solar cells, which trickled energy from sunlight to nickel cadmium batteries, from which the instruments and equipment drew their power. The satellite had one wide and one narrow angle camera, each with a tape recorder for remote operation. The picture data was stored on tape, or transmitted directly to ground command stations. Transmitters were two 2-watt FM units operating at 235 megacycles; also, there were two tracking beacons operating on 108 and 108.03 megacycles with a 30 milliwatt output.

This satellite was the first of a series with which we would test the equipment for experimental television techniques which would eventually lead to a worldwide weather information system with Nimbus, Aeros, and other orbiting vehicles. It proved tremendously successful. It shot into a near-circular orbit, from a perigee of 429.7 miles to an apogee of 467.4 miles. As it circled the earth, its video system relayed more than twenty-two thousand pictures containing photographs of cloud cover, patterns, movement, structure, etc. In meteorological terms, Tiros I was a fabulous creation.

Once again, however, there is a note of caution. The estimated time of Tiros I in orbit as a useful, productive vehicle came to 78 days. No more, no less. At the end of those 78 days the video system no longer functioned. Tiros I became another piece of scrap metal in the heavens.

But if you look at the charts comparing our satellites in orbit with the satellites of our competition, you will notice Tiros I displayed proudly as part of the list. That satellite may be in orbit for another century, give or take some years. During all that time, it will continue to be no more and no less than the chunk of metal it is now. The only purpose it serves at this moment, and will continue to serve, is to bulge the list with another statistic. It means absolutely nothing. The vehicle in orbit must be productive or else it is scrap.

TRANSIT I-B: April 13, 1960

Here we have a satellite that served much of the function of the meteorological satellite test vehicles. Transit is a navigational satellite test item. It was sent into orbit (the first shot failed) to "determine feasibility and equipment for future all-weather global navigational satellites for ships and aircraft." In a terse announcement the Navy revealed that the results of the Transit I-B orbiting "indicate such a navigational system is feasible." If the indications are sustained in continuing tests, then aircraft, ships, and any other vehicle or system will be able to "tune in" to any one of several orbiting Transits, point to a map, and declare "Here I am."

DISCOVERER XIII: August 10, 1960

"Something new" was added to the Discoverer series when the Air Force made its first successful recovery of a payload from space. As part of the broad program of technological development, the Air

Force prepared its Discoverers in such a way that they would eject from orbit a 300-pound capsule, fire a retrorocket within the capsule, send the payload crashing back through the atmosphere, to survive the heat pulse of 11,000 degrees and then be recovered intact. In addition this new capability obviously has great ramifications for the entire national satellite program. It means we will be able to conduct experiments in the space environment and then, aside from telemetered data, also recover the instruments themselves for elaborate laboratory study. At the same time, biopack capsules for the orbiting of animals as well as their recovery was assured by the successful Discoverer XIII mission.

ECHO I: August 12, 1960

"A giant bag of almost-nothing" might aptly describe the Echo balloon, a shiny, superthin sphere of Mylar plastic 100 feet in diameter sent into orbit "for use as a reflector in a series of passive communications satellite experiments." One of the finest orbits ever achieved marked the Echo I experiment (perigee—945 miles, apogee—1,049 miles). Into a 26½-inch magnesium sphere went 132 pounds of mylar plastic, 4 pounds of aluminum covering for the mylar; 30 pounds of powder, which when exposed to sunlight, would turn to gas and inflate the plastic. This comprised the payload of a rocket weighing 112,000 pounds. The end result was the bright and shining sphere that demonstrated the "feasibility of global communications systems using satellites. Aluminum coating designed to provide radio wave reflectivity of 98 percent up to frequencies of 20,000 MC." We bounced radio, telephone, and TV transmissions across the United States with the famous Echo balloon.

COURIER I-B: October 4, 1960

Aside from the scientific-commercial communications projects with satellites (Score, Echo, Telstar, Relay), satellites to meet military communications needs were pressed with the greatest urgency. One such satellite was Courier I-B, a 500-pound sphere ringed with solar cells and crammed with 300 pounds of electronic gadgetry. The terse official announcement of this satellite stated that the mission is to "Test feasibility of global military communications network using 'delayed

repeater' satellites which receive and store information until commanded to transmit." Into the 51-inch-diameter Courier I-B went four
microwave FM transmitters each weighing 26 pounds; four receivers;
five tape recorders; two microwave antennas; a transistorized telemetry
generator; FM VHF telemetry transmitters; four whip antennas (external); VHF diplexer; command decoder; and a 50 mw transistorized
VHF beacon transmitter subsystem. In addition to this, there was spare
equipment to be switched into the system upon ground command. A
total of 19,200 solar cells supplied power to nickel cadmium batteries
for power storage.

It is a military project and obviously a great boon also to outposts in
Antarctica. Cut off from the world by storms as they are, they can
keep in touch with any part of the world through polar orbiting, de-
layed-repeater satellites.

EXPLORER VIII: November 3, 1960

Another in the "scientific research" satellites, Explorer VIII orbited the
earth for "Investigation of the ionosphere by direct measurement of
positive ion and electron composition; [to] gather data on the frequency,
momentum and energy of micrometeorite impacts." Into the 90-pound
satellite (successfully orbited) went: dipole antenna; single-grid ion
trap; four multiple-grid ion traps; electric field meter; photomultiplier;
micrometeorite microphone; four thermistors; sensor to measure electron temperature."

DISCOVERER XVII: November 12, 1960

As the Discoverer series progressed, several Discoverers carried
Doppler beacons and blinking external lights for optical tracking by
powerful cameras to assist in the Transit satellite program. The large
size and weight-lifting capacity of the Thor-Agena B vehicles meant
unexpected dividends to the national space effort. Discoverer XVII's
official mission was a "Systems evaluation of the Agena B satellite including launching techniques, propulsion, communications, orbital performance, recovery techniques and advanced engineering tests." Total
weight in orbit came to 2,100 pounds, of a vehicle 25 feet long and
5 feet in diameter.

As part of scientific experiments, all "surplus" to the primary mission, Discoverer XVII carried a radiation counter and emulsion pack to explore radiation in the lower Van Allen belts; micro-organisms, plant spore, and microscopic, artificially grown human cells; and, a high-intensity light beacon for optical tracking. It was a beautiful shot, including successful recovery of the capsule which re-entered upon command from orbit.

DISCOVERER XVIII: December 7, 1960

This satellite performed the basic mission functions of its predecessor, but added a few extras on the orbital shot. It remained in orbit for 48 circuits of the earth (a trip of 1,250,000 miles) before recovery. As "surplus payload," Discoverer XVIII carried "algae, bone marrow, membrane from underside of eyelid, gamma globulin, spores, gold foil, analine powder and other material for a variety of medical and technical experiments. Included tracking experiment consisting of light beacon for SAO optical tracking."

EXPLORER IX: February 16, 1961

The payload of this 80-pound satellite included a sphere weighing 15 pounds that inflated to a diameter of 12 feet. Here is an instance where a lightweight, seemingly little-important object plays a major role in scientific research. The evaluation of tracking data of this satellite indicated that the density of the upper atmosphere for October, 1961 was about ten times lower than the density as measured eighteen months before. Scientists attributed the decrease to decreased activity of the sun "at this portion of the 11-year solar cycle. Measurements of temperature and density as perturbed by solar activity have been taken continuously and will continue for two more years."

EXPLORER X: March 25, 1961

The basic purpose of scientific research of this 79-pound satellite was complicated by the necessity to extend the research to a great distance from the earth. NASA programmed this satellite to "gather definitive information on Earth and interplanetary magnetic fields and the way these fields affect and are affected by solar plasma."

The satellite went into orbit at 23,900 miles per hour. It soared from its 100-mile perigee to an apogee of 145,000 miles; considerably greater than halfway to the moon. The Mercury space capsules orbited the earth in a period of slightly under 89 minutes. The manner of flight of Explorer X is emphasized when we see that its orbital period to complete one revolution of the earth required 112 hours.

EXPLORER XI: April 27, 1961

The continuing series of Explorer satellites produced this 82-pound package. (It resembled an old-time street lamp in configuration more than a space satellite.) Instruments contained a "gamma ray telescope consisting of a plastic scintillator, crystal layers and a Cerenkov detector; sun and earth sensors; micrometeorite shield; temperature sensor; and a damping mechanism." The mission was to "detect high energy gamma rays from cosmic sources and map their distribution in the sky." Mission accomplished.

DISCOVERER XXV: June 16, 1961

Aboard this military satellite went "rare and common metals to permit study of the effects of space environment on them; also, instruments to measure radiation and micrometeorite effects." This constituted the "surplus payload," which was recovered after re-entry.

TRANSIT IV-A: June 29, 1961

This mission included the orbiting by one booster of three satellites, each of a size and weight permitting boost by a Thor-Ablestar "workhorse" booster. The first satellite—and primary vehicle—was the Transit IV-A to continue the global all-weather navigation satellite system. The second satellite was a spherical, 55-pound package called Greb III carrying instruments to measure solar X-ray radiation. The third satellite, a 40-pound package called Injun, measured cosmic radiation intensities.

There were two interesting sidelights to this mission. Orbiting was completely successful, and Transit IV-A functioned as planned. But a finer study of the mission shows that Greb III and Injun failed to separate and suffered impaired efficiency in their operation.

In addition to its solar cells and nickel cadmium batteries Transit IV-A also carried a radioisotopic-fueled thermoelectric generator—the first satellite known to utilize a nuclear generator as a power source. It measured about 5 inches by 5½ inches, weighed 4½ pounds and used plutonium 238 as fuel.

MERCURY-ATLAS V: November 29, 1961

The last of the unmanned Mercury spacecraft to be orbited before the flight of astronaut John H. Glenn, Jr., in February, 1962, this mission represents the "hard engineering evaluation and checkout" concept for NASA's man-in-space program. The capsule at that time functioned on the basis of automatic and command systems maintaining primary responsibility for a man in space. The man went along essentially as an observer, passive passenger, and a "backup to the robot systems." MA-5 carried the chimpanzee Enos. Scheduled for three orbits, the mission was cut short at the end of two orbits due to an abnormal rolling rate in the capsule, caused by an erratic stabilization system.

TIROS IV: February 8, 1962

Another advanced phase in the development of the weather satellite system, Tiros IV represents a research mission effort that began to pay dividends. The 285-pound satellite, fourth in the series, performed so well that in addition to its primary function as a research vehicle, the pictures from its television cameras were employed to prepare cloud analyses for use in operational weather analysis and forecasting. This step represented one of the first true occasions when the investment began to produce a tangible, working return. The analyses prepared from Tiros IV, and subsequent satellites in the series, were disseminated over domestic and international weather communications circuits. Summing up the capability: Tiros IV showed storms and other conditions around the earth of which weathermen were unaware—including one hurricane spotted by this satellite and not discovered by conventional means until three days later.

ARIEL: April 26, 1962

At first glance Ariel is just another research satellite for the scientific investigation of space. Its mission specifically was to "investigate the ionosphere and its relationships with the Sun." To perform its tasks the 132-pound Ariel carried an "electron density sensor, electron temperature gage, solar aspect sensor, cosmic ray detector, ion mass sphere, Lyman-Alpha gages, tape recorder, X-ray sensors."

The "difference" in Ariel is that this was the first of the international satellites to be launched with U.S. boosters. Project Direction was a joint effort of NASA and the British National Committee for Space Research and there were six British experiments aboard the satellite.

ALOUETTE I: September 29, 1962

The second "satellite with a difference" was Canada's Alouette I—the first satellite designed and built by a nation other than the United States or the Soviet Union. Another "first" in its history is that it was the first NASA-program satellite launched from the west coast of the United States. (The launch vehicle was Air Force Thor-Agena B, as used for the Discoverer program.)

The 320-pound Alouette I went into a high near-circular orbit of 620 miles perigee and 638 miles apogee. The mission was to "study the ionosphere's free electron distribution, measure galactic noise from outer space and in ionosphere, and observe cosmic rays." An ingenious part of the satellite was its antenna system. Two antennas, stored in the form of a carpenter's steel tape, were extended to distances of 75 and 150 feet from the satellite.

EXPLORER XV: October 27, 1962

The second satellite launched to study in detail the effects of artificial nuclear explosions in space, Explorer XV was sent into orbit after the effects of atomic and hydrogen bombs produced radiation so severe that it had completely blanketed the capacity of several satellites still orbiting, and eliminated their further usefulness (another notation to mark on the chart of numbers of satellites in orbit).

The official mission was terse: "Study artificial radiation belt created by July 9 nuclear explosion." Explorer XV had instruments to carry out "experiments to survey electron energy distribution, omnidirectional intensity of electrons and protons, angular distribution of electron flux, particle flux, solar cell damage, and magnetic field." It looped about the earth with a perigee of 193.7 miles and an apogee of 10,760 miles.

THE LUNAR PROBES

Concerning plans, missions, roles, and hopes of the United States' lunar probes, there is much to write about. But concerning information gathered and results, there is little more than embarrassment. The lunar probe program of the United States has been beset with the most exasperating and frustrating collection of failures of any effort to date in the space age.

A review of these missions is best accomplished by a brief résumé of each:

AUGUST 17, 1958

The first lunar probe, using a Thor-Able booster, carried a two-fold mission. First we had to achieve proper performance from the three-stage rocket (first of its kind in the United States for a major space effort). This done, we had to establish precise trajectory control in order to send the payload to the vicinity of the moon. Because of the untried rocket assembly and lack of experience, a flight to within 50,000 miles of the moon would be considered an "overwhelming success." The 83.8-pound payload in the shape of a toroid carried an electronic device to scan the lunar surface; instruments to measure magnetic fields of the Earth and moon; micrometeorite density recorders; internal temperature recorders; vernier rockets for velocity-orbit control; and an injection rocket to place the toroid in orbit about the moon.

Seventy-seven seconds after launching, the first flight of Project Mona vanished in a thundering explosion ten miles above Cape Canaveral.

OCTOBER 11, 1958

In a repeat attempt to reach the moon, Project Mona sent its second lunar probe into space two months after its initial rocket blew up. This time the rocket traveled slightly less than one-third of the distance to its target. The 84.4-pound toroid, officially named Pioneer I in celebration of its partial success, lofted out to a distance of 70,700 miles from the earth.

As a lunar probe Pioneer I failed. Scientists were quick to label the attempt as a "magnificent failure," and for once the bizarre attribution of "success" to "failure" contained some merit. Pioneer I traveled the greatest distance from the Earth of a functioning space vehicle. The toroid transmitted extensive data back to Earth. It charted the radiation bands beyond the planet; provided the first mapping of the "total ionizing flux"; made the first observation of hydromagnetic oscillations of Earth's magnetic field; made the first micrometeor density measurements in "outer space"; and made the first measurements of the interplanetary magnetic field.

NOVEMBER 8, 1958

Pioneer II received its official title (no names were given to shots that failed) not because it was successful, but because engineers thought it was successful. Information transmitted from the ascending rocket showed the third stage to have ignited and pushed the toroid payload to escape velocity from the Earth. Press releases rained like confetti on Cape Canaveral. Several minutes after the word flashed around the world that the first probe was on its way to the moon, an unhappy officer explained that it was all a "horrible mistake." The lunar probe crashed back to Earth 42 minutes after it left Canaveral.

DECEMBER 6, 1958

With three up and three down for the Air Force, the Army stepped into the moon business with two Juno II boosters. It was necessary to look twice to be certain that one was really seeing the lunar probe vehicle, for it was a diminutive conical structure of gold-washed fiberglas that weighed exactly 12.95 pounds. Within the cone were two Geiger-Muller tubes and associated circuitry to measure corpuscular radiation in space; a photoelectric sensing device to be triggered by light reflected from the moon; and a radio transmitter.

Pioneer III made it out to 63,580 miles, and fell back into the Earth's atmosphere 38 hours after launch. One unexpected dividend: the little cone discovered that there existed a second, outer radiation belt around the planet.

MARCH 3, 1959

The fifth lunar probe—the 13.4-pound Pioneer IV—was the first to *achieve escape velocity*. Its booster accelerated the little cone to 24,790 miles per hour. As the cone sped away from the earth, it transmitted data on radiation levels in space. But once again the experiments assigned to Pioneer IV failed as a lunar probe. The tiny package sped past the moon at a distance of 37,300 miles. None of the instruments installed for lunar studies operated.

SEPTEMBER 24, 1959

Number Six in the series was to be a tremendous jump in payload (372 pounds), and in control. The first Atlas-Able rocket went to the lunar program, and with this giant, hopes soared for a success. On September 24, 1959, the rocket underwent a static firing of maximum engine thrust but with the vehicle bolted securely to its launch stand. The first Atlas-Able rocket never went into space. The Atlas burned, fell over from its launch stand, and exploded violently. The tremendous blast wrecked the launch facilities.

NOVEMBER 26, 1959

The second lunar probe for the Atlas-Able series carried in its 372 pounds four vanes with 8,800 solar cells; a small engine for in-flight velocity corrections and thrust reversal to enter into orbit about the moon; a micrometeorite counter; high-energy radiation counter; total radiation flux counter; low energy radiation counter; photo-scanning device; magnetometers; aspect indicator; receiver for natural (background) radio waves; two transmitters; and, nickel cadmium batteries.

Forty-five seconds after launch, a protective fairing around the payload ripped off the climbing rocket. Friction set fire and tore loose the lunar probe, and broke away the third stage rocket. Several minutes later the vehicle crashed back into the ocean.

SEPTEMBER 25, 1960

The payload increased to 387 pounds in weight; some instruments were replaced with improved devices and hopes remained high. The second stage burned improperly, and the needed velocity was not reached. The official summary for the flight stated: "Vehicle either burned up on re-entry or disintegrated on impact."

DECEMBER 15, 1960

In the fourth and final shot with the Atlas-Able, with a duplicate payload of the previous attempt, the rocket launched perfectly. Sixty-eight seconds after liftoff, the second stage exploded. Three seconds later, the Atlas exploded. The wreckage landed in the ocean about ten miles from the launch pad. The Atlas-Able series ended, marking the ninth attempt to explore the vicinity of the moon—and the ninth consecutive failure.

AUGUST 23, 1961

The new vehicle was called Ranger I, and the new booster was the powerful Atlas-Agena B which had scored great success in satellite launchings. Rangers I and II were not specifically lunar probes; they were deep space probes. However, the official listing of their major objectives was the "Development of spacecraft systems for future lunar and interplanetary missions . . ." In the course of this development the Rangers would be sent on a swooping elliptical orbit a half-million miles from Earth to "investigate cosmic rays, radiation and dust particles in space, as well as whether Earth is trailed by comet-like tail of hydrogen gas."

The flight program called for the Agena to inject into a low earth orbit—the so-called parking orbit. After all details of the orbit were determined by computers, the command signal to reignite the Agena engine would be given; Agena would then accelerate to near-escape velocity speed.

The payload soared to 675 pounds in a cone with a hexagonal base, five feet in diameter and eleven feet long. The instruments would give: "Experiments in solar radiation, particle detection, cosmic rays, magnetic fields, solar X-rays, neutral hydrogen geocorona, cosmic dust, and friction in space."

Ranger I went into an excellent low earth orbit with a perigee of 105.3 miles and a velocity of 17,726 miles per hour. The attempt to reignite the Agena engine failed. Ranger I remained in its low Earth orbit for seven days, and then burned on re-entry into the atmosphere.

NOVEMBER 18, 1961

Ranger II lifted from Cape Canaveral at 3:12 A.M. Injection into orbit was successful, with a perigee of 94.9 miles. The attempt to re-ignite the Agena engine failed. Ranger II later that same day burned on re-entry into the atmosphere.

JANUARY 26, 1962

Ranger III was the first of a series of new vehicles with extensive missions planned. The spacecraft weight went up to 727 pounds. The payload went onto its hexagonal base "on which are placed, successively, conical mid-course motor, cylindrical retrorocket, spherical lunar capsule and conical omnidirectional antenna." Several transmitters were installed, and power came from large "wings" fitted with 8,680 solar cells, a 25-pound silver zinc battery, and six silver cadmium batteries.

The objective was impact on the lunar surface. TV cameras would transmit pictures to Earth during the plunge into the moon's surface. X-ray spectroscopy would be carried out all the way to the moon. Extensive engineering experiments would be conducted in attitude control, mid-course, and terminal guidance. A survivable capsule containing a seismometer was to be rough-landed on the lunar surface to transmit data on tremors, quakes, and meteor impacts.

Ranger III missed the moon by a distance of 22,862 miles. All experiments save limited transmissions of gamma-ray data failed.

APRIL 23, 1962

Ranger IV was injected along an accurate trajectory to the moon. All mid-course and terminal guidance attempts failed. Power systems failed. All scientific experiments failed. The 730-pound spacecraft tumbled uselessly in uncontrolled gyrations toward the moon. Scientists believe that as it passed around the far side of the moon it "button-hooked" down to crash to the lunar surface. The official summary of the flight is to the point:

"Impact occurred at a point *calculated* as 229.3° E. longitude and 15.5° S. latitude. No scientific data obtained."

OCTOBER 18, 1962

Ranger V injection into parking orbit successful; departure from parking orbit successful; injection into trans-lunar trajectory successful. Eight hours after launch, power supply system of lunar probe failed. On October 21, Ranger V fell past the moon at a distance of 450 miles. All mid-course and terminal guidance attempts failed. Entered into solar orbit. No data on lunar investigations obtained.

RANGER SCHEDULE FOR THE FUTURE

Ranger VI canceled. Eight additional Ranger vehicles planned; extensive study and redesign of spacecraft systems involved.

INDEX